RUN FOREVER

Coordinating Author
Jack Booth

David Booth
Jo Phenix & Larry Swartz

IMPRESSIONS

HOLT, RINEHART AND WINSTON OF CANADA
a division of
Harcourt Brace & Company Canada, Ltd.
Toronto, Orlando, San Diego, London, Sydney

Cover Illustrator: Doug Martin

ISBN: 0–03–921902–X

Copyright © 1986 Holt, Rinehart and Winston of Canada. A Division of Harcourt Brace & Company Canada, Ltd.

Canadian Cataloguing in Publication Data

Main entry under title:
Run forever

(Impressions)
For use in schools.
ISBN 0–03–921902–X

1. Readers (Elementary).   I. Booth, Jack, 1946–
II. Series: Impressions (Toronto, Ont.)

PE1119.R86 1986   428.6   C86–093583–3

Illustrations
Lisa Smith: pp. 6-7; *Michael Reinhart:* pp. 8-15; *Molly Bang: 16-21; Vladyana Krykorka:* pp. 22-25; *Laura Fernandez:* pp. 26-32; *Richard daMota:* pp. 33-39; *Magda Markowski:* pp. 40-41; *Martin Gould:* pp. 42-43; *Brock Cole:* pp. 44-50; *Henry van der Linde:* pp. 51-61, 116-117, 184-189; *San Murata:* pp. 62-63, 250-255; *Margaret Hathaway:* pp. 64-65, 234-239; *Ron Barrett:* pp. 66-71; *Allen Shugar:* pp. 72-73; *Diane Goode:* pp. 74-77; *Kathryn Adams:* pp. 78-79; *Paul McCusker:* pp. 80-83, 126-137; *Jeff Pickerman:* pp. 84-93; *Ken Stampnick:* pp. 94-95, 166-173; *Ron Berg:* pp. 96-97, 256-267; *Michael Cutler:* pp. 98-101; *Steve Huston:* pp. 102-113; *Kellie Jobson:* pp. 114-115; *Donald Carrick:* pp. 118-125; *Mike Constable:* pp. 138-139; *William Kimber:* pp. 140-145, 162-165; *Paul Goble:* pp. 146-153; *Barry Rubin:* pp. 154-155; *Garth Williams:* pp. 156-161; *Barbara Klunder:* pp. 174-175; *Nick Vitacco:* pp. 176-177, 190-191, 218-229; *Kent Smith:* pp. 178-181; *Rene Zamic:* pp. 182-183; *Fiona French:* pp. 192-207; *Victor Gad:* pp. 208-209; *Joanna Stubbs:* pp. 210-217; *Laurie LaFrance:* pp. 230-231; *Doug Martin:* pp. 232-233; *Aliki:* pp. 240-247; *Jamie Bennet:* pp. 248-249, 268-269; *Lloyd Bloom:* pp. 270-279; *Ezra Jack:* pp. 280-285; *Jerzy Kolacz:* pp. 286-287.

The authors and publishers gratefully acknowledge the educators listed below for their contribution to the development of this program:
Ron Benson   *Coordinator of Primary Education   Scarborough Board of Education*
Ethel Buchanan   *Language Arts Consultant   Winnipeg, Manitoba*
Margaret Crocker   *Teacher and Vice Principal   Bedford District School Board Halifax County*
William Fagan   *Language Arts Coordinator   Roman Catholic School Board for St. John's Newfoundland*
Ruth Fulton   *Supervisor of Elementary Education   District No. 20, Saint John, New Brunswick*
June Gravel   *Language Arts Coordinator   Dufferin-Peel Roman Catholic Separate School Board*
Pat Hogan   *Language Arts Consultant   Calgary Board of Education Coordinator Calgary Writing Project*
Margaret Joyce   *Language Arts Consultant   School Unit No. 3, Charlottetown, P.E.I.*
Linda Kaser   *Coordinator, Language Arts and English K-12   Richmond School District*
Roberta McKay   *Consultant, Language Arts/Social Studies   Edmonton Public Schools*
Ina Mary Rutherford   *Supervisor of Reading and Primary Education   Bruce County Board of Education*
Janice Petracek   *Executive Assistant to the Deputy Director of Education   Regina School Division*

Printed in Canada   5 6 7 8 98 97 96

TABLE OF CONTENTS

OUT OF THE WOODS   *David Booth*...................................... 6
Greyling   *Jane Yolen*.. 8
Dawn   *Molly Bang* 16
Tell Me, Tell Me, Sarah Jane   *Charles Causley*.................... 22
Little John Bottlejohn   *Laura E. Richards*.......................... 24
Ti-Jean and the White Cat   *Eva Martin* 26
Halibut Man and the House on the Waves   *Dorothy de Wit*.... 33
The Fish of the Sea   *Traditional* 40
The Will   *Ian Serraillier*... 42
The Winter Wren   *Brock Cole* 44
The Flying Horse Machine   *Barbara Winther*...................... 51
Recess: Rhymes of Old   *Traditional* 62

LIKE ALL THE OTHERS   *David Booth*............................. 64
Old MacDonald Had an Apartment House   *Judith Barrett*..... 66
The Rainbow Connection   *Paul Williams and*
     Kenny Ascher 72
When I Was Young in the Mountains   *Cynthia Rylant*.......... 74
A Revolving Door   *Lola Sneyd*.. 78
Storm Over Lake Ontario   *Lola Sneyd*.............................. 78
Street Action   *Lola Sneyd*.. 79
Home   *Douglas Young*... 80
The General   *Frank Etherington*...................................... 84
The Unbelievable   *Raymond Souster* 94
Nobody's Told the Birds   *Raymond Souster*........................ 95
Peewee   *Suzanne Martel*... 96
Hockey Masks   *Michael Cutler* 98
Gretzky   *Meguido Zola*.. 102
Recess: Skipping Rhymes   *Traditional* 114

THE BACK OF THE CAVE   *David Booth* 116

Patrick's Dinosaurs   *Carol Carrick* 118

Dinosaurs   *Keith Moseley* 126

Highway Construction (As Emily Dickinson Might
   React to It)   *Carole Earle Chapin* 138

Long Gone   *Jack Prelutsky* 138

Brontosaurus   *Gail Kredenser* 139

People of the Buffalo: How the Plains Indians Lived
   Maria Campbell 140

Buffalo Woman   *Paul Goble* 146

The Bone Gatherers   *David Booth* 154

Red River Cart Song   *Lorraine Johnson* 155

Little House on the Prairie   *Laura Ingalls Wilder* 156

A Letter from the Coast   *Laura Ingalls Wilder* 162

That Scatterbrain Booky   *Bernice Thurman Hunter* 166

Recess: Jingles   *Traditional* 174

ONE DAY AFTER   *David Booth* 176

Robots   *Paula Taylor* 178

Tomorrow   *Martin Charnin* 182

The Iron Man   *Ted Hughes* 184

Moon Poem   *Saundra Sharp* 190

Tell Me a Story   *Eve Merriam* 191

Future Story   *Fiona French* 192

Zachary Zed   *James Reeves* 208

U.F.O.   *Joanna Stubbs* 210

Space Trap   *Monica Hughes* 218

Recess: Counting Rhymes   *Traditional* 230

ALL THE PEOPLE WE MEET *David Booth* 232

Tale of a Shipwrecked Sailor *Ron Lynd* 234

Mummies Made in Egypt *Aliki* 240

Queen Nefertiti *Anonymous* 248

If You Should Meet a Crocodile *Anonymous* 249

The Crocodile *Lewis Carroll* 249

A Boy Called Nam *Leo Heaps* 250

In the Land of Small Dragon *Dang Muhn Kha* 256

Ethiopian Proverbs *Traditional* 268

Nadia the Willful *Sue Alexander* 270

The King's Fountain *Lloyd Alexander* 280

Recess: Songs *Traditional* 286

Acknowledgements 288

OUT OF THE WOODS

Some stories were never really written by anyone. Instead, they were told aloud: passed down by word of mouth, until someone decided to write them down so that they wouldn't be lost. Every country has folklore from the past that has been preserved, just as you have favourite stories about your family that you tell at family gatherings. Over the years the stories change, but still the past clings to them, and we can use them as stepping stones to other times and other places. The following excerpt is from a Russian folk tale, but it might remind you of similar stories from your own background.

Vasilisa walked the entire day, and it was not until evening that she reached the clearing where Baba Yaga's hut stood. It was surrounded by a fence made of human bones topped by human skulls. Leg bones made up the gateposts, skeletons' hands served as bolts, and instead of a lock there was a mouth with sharp teeth. Vasilisa grew faint with fear and stood rooted to the spot. Suddenly a horseman rode up. He was black, his clothes were

black, and he was mounted on a black horse. He rode right up to Baba Yaga's gates—and disappeared as if he had fallen through the earth. And immediately night fell. But the darkness did not last long. The skulls' eyes lit up, and it became as bright in the clearing as if it were noon. Vasilisa trembled with fear, but not knowing where to flee she stayed where she was.

Soon a terrible noise came from the forest. The trees creaked and the dry leaves crackled. Out of the woods came Baba Yaga riding in a mortar, pushing her way along with a pestle and sweeping the tracks it left behind with a broom. She rode up to the gates, stopped, sniffed and cried out:

"Foo, foo, I smell a Russian! Who is here?"

(from *Vasilisa the Beautiful*, translated by Thomas P. Whitney)

Well, did you think of other tales as you read this one? Can you predict what will happen in this folk story?

This section is all about folklore. Out of the woods of years gone by come tales like these once more.

GREYLING

by Jane Yolen

Once on a time when wishes were aplenty, a fisherman and his wife lived by the side of the sea. All that they ate came out of the sea. Their hut was covered with the finest mosses that kept them cool in the summer and warm in the winter. And there was nothing they needed or wanted except a child.

Each morning, when the moon slipped down behind the water, and the sun rose up behind the plains, the wife would say to the fisherman, "You have your boat and your nets and your lines. But I have no baby to hold in my arms." And again, in the evening, it was the same. She would weep and wail and rock the cradle that stood by the hearth. But year in and year out the cradle stayed empty.

Now the fisherman was also sad that they had no child. But he kept his sorrow to himself so that his wife would not know his grief and thus doubt her own. Indeed, he would leave the hut each morning with a breath of song and return each night with a whistle on his lips. His nets were full but his heart was empty, yet he never told his wife.

One sunny day, when the beach was a tan thread spun between sea and plain, the fisherman as usual went down to his boat. But this day he found a small grey seal stranded on the sand bar, crying for its own.

The fisherman looked up the beach and down. He looked in front of him and behind. And he looked to the town on the great grey cliffs that sheered off into the sea. But there were no other seals in sight.

So he shrugged his shoulders and took off his shirt. Then he dipped it into the water and wrapped the seal pup carefully into its folds.

"You have no father and you have no mother," he said. "And I have no child. So you shall come home with me."

And the fisherman did no fishing that day but brought the seal

pup, wrapped in his shirt, straight home to his wife.

When she saw him coming home early with no shirt on, the fisherman's wife ran out of the hut. Then she looked wonderingly at the bundle which he held in his arms.

"It is nothing," he said, "but a seal pup I found stranded in the shallows and longing for its own. I thought we could give it love and care until it is old enough to seek its kin."

The fisherman's wife nodded and took the bundle. Then she uncovered the wrapping and gave a loud cry. "Nothing!" she said. "You call this nothing?"

The fisherman looked. Instead of a seal lying in the folds, there was a strange child with great grey eyes and silvery grey hair, smiling up at him.

The fisherman wrung his hands. "It is a selchie," he cried. "I have heard of them. They are men upon the land and seals in the sea. I thought it was but a tale."

"Then he shall remain a man upon the land," said the fisherman's wife, clasping the child in her arms, "for I shall never let him return to the sea."

"Never," agreed the fisherman, for he knew how his wife had wanted a child. And in his secret heart, he wanted one, too. Yet he felt, somehow, it was wrong.

"We shall call him Greyling," said the fisherman's wife, "for his eyes and hair are the colour of a storm-coming sky. Greyling, though he has brought sunlight into our home."

And though they still lived by the side of the water in a hut covered with mosses that kept them warm in the winter and cool in the summer, the boy Greyling was never allowed in the sea.

He grew from a child to a lad. He grew from a lad to a young man. He gathered driftwood for his mother's hearth and searched the tide pools for shells for her mantel. He mended his father's nets and tended his father's boat. But though he often stood by the shore or high in the town on the great grey cliffs, looking and longing and grieving his heart for what he did not really know, he never went into the sea.

Then one wind-wailing morning, just fifteen years from the day that Greyling had been found, a great storm blew up suddenly in the North. It was such a storm as had never been seen before; the sky turned nearly black and even the fish had trouble swimming. The wind pushed huge waves onto the shore. The waters gobbled up the little hut on the beach. And Greyling and the fisherman's wife were forced to flee to the town high on the great grey cliffs. There they looked down at the rolling, boiling sea. Far from shore they spied the fisherman's boat, its sails flapping like the wings of a wounded gull. And clinging to the broken mast was the fisherman himself, sinking deeper with every wave.

The fisherman's wife gave a terrible cry. "Will no one save him?" she called to the people of the town who had gathered on the edge of the cliff. "Will no one save my own dear husband who is all of life to me?"

But the townsmen looked away. There was no man there who dared risk his life in that sea, even to save a drowning soul.

"Will no one at all save him?" she cried out again.

"Let the boy go," said one old man, pointing at Greyling with his stick. "He looks strong enough."

But the fisherman's wife clasped Greyling in her arms and held his ears with her hands. She did not want him to go into the sea. She was afraid he would never return.

But shaking their heads, the people of the town edged to their houses and shut their doors and locked their windows and set their backs to the ocean and their faces to the fires that glowed in every hearth.

"I will save him, Mother," cried Greyling, "or die as I try."

Before she could tell him to stop, he broke from her grasp and dived from the top of the great cliffs, down, down, down into the tumbling sea.

"He will surely sink," whispered the women as they ran from their warm fires to watch.

"He will certainly drown," called the men as they took down

their spyglasses from the shelves.

They gathered on the cliffs and watched the boy dive down into the sea.

As Greyling disappeared beneath the waves, little fingers of foam tore at his clothes. They snatched his shirt, his trousers and his shoes and sent them bubbling away to the shore. And as Greyling went deeper beneath the waves, even his skin seemed to slough off till he swam, free at last, in the sleek grey coat of a great grey seal.

The selchie had returned to the sea.

But the people of the town did not see this. All they saw was the diving boy disappearing under the waves and then, farther out, a large seal swimming towards the boat that wallowed in the sea. The sleek grey seal, with no effort at all, eased the fisherman to the shore, though the waves were wild and bright with foam. And then, with a final salute, it turned its back on the land and headed joyously out to sea.

The fisherman's wife hurried down to the sand. And behind her followed the people of the town. They searched up the beach and down, but they did not find the boy.

"A brave son," said the men when they found his shirt, for they thought he was certainly drowned.

"A very brave son," said the women when they found his shoes, for they thought him lost for sure.

"Has he really gone?" asked the fisherman's wife of her husband when at last they were alone.

"Yes, quite gone," the fisherman said to her. "Gone where his heart calls, gone to the great wide sea. And though my heart grieves at his leaving, it tells me this way is best."

The fisherman's wife sighed. And then she cried. But at last she agreed that, perhaps, it was best. "For he is both man and seal," she said. "And though we cared for him for a while, now he must care for himself." And she never cried again.

So once more they lived alone by the side of the sea in a new little hut which was covered with mosses to keep them warm in the winter and cool in the summer.

Yet, once a year, a great grey seal is seen at night near the fisherman's home. And the people in town talk of it, and wonder. But seals do come to the shore and men do go to the sea; and so the townfolk do not dwell upon it very long.

But it is no ordinary seal. It is Greyling himself come home—come to tell his parents tales of the lands that lie far beyond the waters, and to sing them songs of the wonders that lie far beneath the sea.

DAWN

by Molly Bang

"A long time ago, Dawn, before you were born, I used to build ships. Not little sailboats like I do now, but schooners that carried ice and rocks and lumber up and down the coast. I got the wood for the planking from the cedar swamp. Straight and tall the trees were then, not a branch for thirty feet.

"One day I was in the swamp when I saw a Canada goose in the water near me. Geese need open space; they should never be in the swamp. The bird had been shot and its wing was broken. It could scarcely move. I picked it up, carried it home, and nursed it back to health. In a few weeks it flew away.

"Time went by. One morning a young woman came into the yard and asked if I needed a sailmaker. She was dressed very oddly, with a heavy brown cloak over a dress as pink as your cheeks. She had a long, slender neck and tiny teeth, delicate and white. She had a scar on her arm. I noticed it when she took off her cloak. How could I know what it was from?

"The woman said she could sew sails and could weave the cloth for them if there was a loom to work on. It happened I did need a sailmaker, but I never thought I'd find one like her. The cloth she wove was the finest and toughest I'd ever seen, and the sails she cut fit the wind like they were born there. The boats would almost fly with her sails.

"That was your mother, Dawn. We were married, and before long she gave birth to you. When I saw the pains coming I ran for the midwife, but by the time we got back, you were already born.

"I built a sailboat for the three of us, the one that's yours now. When it was finished, your mother brought out a set of sails she'd made to surprise me. I didn't see how she made them, but never before had I seen such sails. So light and fine and yet so strong they were that people called them Wings of Steel. All that summer and

the next we sailed our boat through the coves and inlets where you sail alone now. How happy we were!

"Then one day a man came to the yard. He showed me plans for a yacht he wanted me to build. It was a racing schooner, with the sleekest lines I ever saw on a hull. He wanted a full set of sails as well, but he wanted sails like our Wings of Steel. Your mother told him no. She said she only made that cloth once, for us, and she couldn't do it again. The man left, mad as a hornet.

"Child, the picture of that boat wouldn't leave me. I pleaded with your mother to make the sails, just this once. She said no, it would take too much out of her. What nonsense, I thought. I kept after her, and at last she relented. She told me it might be the death of her, but I didn't believe her. How beautiful she was then, with her round black eyes and her black, black hair. Before we began, she asked me one thing: never to come into the room while she was weaving the sails. I promised I never would.

"The boat was due on the first of August. The two of us set to work, your mother on the sails and I on the hull. You went from one to the other of us, getting into the wood shavings and holding tools for me. I don't know what you did with your mother. Time went by, the boat grew, and the cloth was rolling off the loom as fast as your mother could weave it. But sometime in June, she began to get weaker, like she said she would.

"At last there were only three days left. The hull and all the sails were ready, except the jib. But your mother had slowed down, and it looked like she wouldn't be finished in time. I got angry. I'd never had a job this big, never a racing schooner. I wanted it to be perfect. Your mother told me not to worry, that the sail would be ready by noon of August first. But she would have to work straight until then, and I was to remember my promise not to come into the room while she was weaving. She looked so thin then. Her dress was scarlet; I thought she'd bought a new one.

"One day went by, and the next. Night fell, and she kept working. I put you to bed and lay down myself, and all the while I could hear the thumping of the loom, slow and regular. I got up in the

middle of the night and went for a walk. Why am I pushing her like this? I thought. I went to her and called for her to stop, to come to bed, to rest. But all I heard was the slow thumping. I went back to bed, and when I woke up the next morning, I could still hear the loom.

"We had breakfast, you and I, and the man came about nine o'clock. He looked the boat over and was satisfied with everything. But he wanted to see the jib. It was the last sail. About eleven-thirty we knocked on your mother's door, but only the sound of the loom answered us. It was working so slowly I could hardly hear it. We went back outside. Finally I couldn't wait any longer. I left you both and went to her room. It was almost twelve. Why couldn't I have waited? I threw open the door. What I saw there, Dawn, I've seen every night since. I'll see it until I die.

"It wasn't your mother at the loom—not the woman I knew. It was a great Canada goose, who was plucking the last feathers from her breast and weaving them into sailcloth. All featherless it was— a pitiful thing to see. The goose turned and looked at me, and shuddered.

"Suddenly I heard a thunderous flapping outside, and a flock of geese flew into the room. You came in just then, Dawn. Your mother ran toward you with her wings outspread, but I caught her in my arms. She hissed and beat at me with her beak, but I held on. I didn't understand what was happening, you see. I just didn't want to lose her, and I didn't want to lose you either. At last she fell quiet and I set her down. All at once the other geese crowded around her and carried her off. I never saw her again."

Dawn's father stopped speaking. He looked out at the blue September sky, still and perfect in the twilight.

After a while, Dawn spoke, "I'll bring her back, Father. I'll go in the boat you made for the three of us. We'll be back in the spring, when the geese come north again."

And so she set off.

TELL ME, TELL ME, SARAH JANE

by Charles Causley

Tell me, tell me, Sarah Jane,
　　Tell me, dearest daughter,
Why are you holding in your hand
　　A thimbleful of water?
Why do you hold it to your eye
　　And gaze both late and soon
From early morning light until
　　The rising of the moon?

Mother, I hear the mermaids cry,
　　I hear the mermen sing,
And I can see the sailing-ships
　　All made of sticks and string.
And I can see the jumping fish,
　　The whales that fall and rise
And swim about the waterspout
　　That swarms up to the skies.

Tell me, tell me, Sarah Jane,
    Tell your darling mother,
Why do you walk beside the tide
    As though you loved none other?
Why do you listen to a shell
    and watch the billows curl,
And throw away your diamond ring
    And wear instead the pearl?

Mother I hear the water
    beneath the headland pinned,
And I can see the sea-gull
    Sliding down the wind.
I taste the salt upon my tongue
    As sweet as sweet can be.

Tell me, my dear, whose voice you hear?

It is the sea, the sea.

LITTLE JOHN BOTTLEJOHN

by Laura E. Richards

Little John Bottlejohn lived on the hill,
    And a blithe little man was he.
And he won the heart of a pretty mermaid
    Who lived in the deep blue sea.
And every evening she used to sit
    And sing by the rocks of the sea,
"Oh! little John Bottlejohn, pretty John Bottlejohn,
    Won't you come out to me?"

Little John Bottlejohn heard her song,
    And he opened his little door,
And he hopped and he skipped, and he skipped and he hopped,
    Until he came down to the shore.
And there on the rocks sat the little mermaid,
    And still she was singing so free,
"Oh! little John Bottlejohn, pretty John Bottlejohn,
    Won't you come out to me?"

Little John Bottlejohn made a bow,
　　And the mermaid, she made one too;
And she said, "Oh! I never saw anyone half
　　So perfectly sweet as you!
In my lovely home 'neath the ocean foam,
　　How happy we both might be!
Oh! little John Bottlejohn, pretty John Bottlejohn,
　　Won't you come down with me?"

　　Little John Bottlejohn said, "Oh yes!
　　　　I'll willingly go with you,
　　And I never shall quail at the sight of your tail,
　　　　For perhaps I may grow one, too."
　　So he took her hand, and he left the land,
　　　　And he plunged in the foaming main.
　　And little John Bottlejohn, pretty John Bottlejohn,
　　　　Never was seen again.

TI-JEAN AND THE WHITE CAT

retold by Eva Martin

O nce upon a time, in a kingdom far away, there lived an old
king who had neither sons nor daughters to inherit his crown.
So he invited all the fine young men of the land to come to his castle
so he could look them over and decide who was best suited to be the
next king. And of all the young men who came, there were three
who were so perfect that the king couldn't choose from among them.
One of them was that rascal, Ti-Jean. The king looked over the three
young men, scratched his beard, and thought and thought. Finally
he said, "Off you go down the road, you young fellows. Whoever
brings back the finest horse in the land will be the next king."

The three fellows set off eagerly down the road. After a while they came to a place where the road divided into three. Each fellow chose a different road to travel down. Ti-Jean sauntered on and on until he came to the end of the road. There he found a little path that led through the forest. He walked down the path until he came to a thatched cottage. There in the yard of the cottage were a white cat and four toads. They were all helping to fill a tub with water. After a while, out of the tub came the most beautiful princess that Ti-Jean had ever seen.

The princess looked at Ti-Jean and said, "What are you looking for?"

"I'm looking for a horse, that's what I'm looking for. The king promised that whoever brings back the most beautiful horse in the land will inherit his crown."

"Well, tomorrow morning I will turn into a white cat again," the princess said. "When I do, go into the stable and take away the ugliest toad that you can find there. Take him back to the king's castle and the next morning, when you lead him before the king, he will be the finest horse you have ever seen."

The next morning, Ti-Jean went into the stable and selected the ugliest toad he could find. You can imagine how his two rivals laughed when he met them at the crossroads.

"You'd better be careful," they said, "for when the king sees you riding that toad, he may think you're making fun of him and have you put to death."

Ti-Jean just smiled. He rode on his toad and whipped him along with a piece of string. When the three young men arrived at the king's castle, Ti-Jean put his toad in the stable and took a comb and curried him as best he could.

"Be careful of the king's comb," jeered the other two fellows. "You might break it."

The next morning the three young fellows got up and prepared to meet the king. The king admired the two beautiful horses that the first two young men had brought. "Now Ti-Jean, my fine fellow," he said, "Where is your horse?"

"Oh," the others laughed, "you'll never guess. He actually rode in on a toad."

"A toad," said the king. "Come, come, I must see that for sure."

Ti-Jean went to the stable and came back leading the most magnificent horse anybody had ever seen. Its hooves were gold and its mane was of silver.

"Well, it's obvious," said the king, "that Ti-Jean has won this test, but you know a king always devises three tests. So there are two more to go. Now, whoever brings me the finest homespun will inherit my crown."

Ti-Jean and the other two young men went off down the same road, and when they came to the fork, they each took the same road they had before. Ti-Jean wandered down the long path until he came to the same little thatched house. Again he saw the white cat and the four toads filling the tub with water. Ti-Jean watched the white cat and, as she had the day before, when the tub was filled with water she jumped in and emerged the most beautiful princess Ti-Jean had ever seen.

"Hello, there," she said. "Ti-Jean, now what are you looking for?"

"I took the king the most beautiful horse in the world, and now he wants the finest homespun ever made before I can inherit his crown."

"Very well," said the princess. "Tomorrow morning I will turn into a cat again. Go and look in the big chest in the barn and select the ugliest walnut that you can find. Take it with you and when you go before the king, open it with a sharp knife. You will find thirty yards of the finest homespun you have ever seen."

The next day, Ti-Jean selected the ugliest walnut and put it in his pocket. When he met his two rivals at the crossroads, they laughed and they jeered, for they saw that Ti-Jean had nothing.

At the castle, the first two fellows showed the king the beautiful homespun they had found. Then they said, "That fellow, Ti-Jean, he doesn't have anything to show."

With twinkling eyes, Ti-Jean put his hand in his pocket and

brought forth the walnut. He placed it in the king's hand and said, "Take a knife, Your Majesty, cut it open and you will see what you shall see." The king broke open the walnut, and there flowed forth thirty yards of the finest homespun he had ever seen.

"Ti-Jean wins again, but there is still the third task. This time, whoever brings back the most beautiful princess for a bride will inherit my crown."

They all hurried off down the road again and when they came to the crossroads, each went down the same road as before. Ti-Jean travelled and travelled until he came to the cottage with the straw thatch. There he saw the big white cat carrying water and filling the tub as before. She jumped into the tub and emerged as a beautiful princess. By this time, Ti-Jean had fallen madly in love with her.

"Well, now, Ti-Jean," she said. "What did you come for this time?"

"The king has given me a third task. He says that whoever brings back the most beautiful princess for a bride will inherit his crown. You are the most beautiful girl I've ever seen in my life."

"I turn into a cat every morning, and I can never be a princess again unless a king agrees to marry me."

"That's all right," said Ti-Jean. "You just come with me."

"Tomorrow," she said, "I will turn into a big white cat again. You harness those four toads to the old coach in the stable and we will go together."

The next morning, Ti-Jean found the four toads and harnessed them to the old coach. He placed the white cat in the coach, where she purred contentedly. Then he got up and with a little bit of string, he whipped up the toads and off they travelled down the path.

The other two young men had very nice-looking girls. They looked at Ti-Jean and the white cat and the four toads and they sneered, "Well, the king will take one look and that will be the end of you. Don't follow close to us. We'll be the laughing stock of the village."

Ti-Jean just grinned from ear to ear as he whipped up the toads with his piece of string. Finally they arrived at the castle. Ti-Jean took the toads and the white cat to the stable and he groomed the toads with his comb.

"Ti-Jean," said the other two, "you'll break the king's comb."

"Oh," said Ti-Jean, "it may be my comb soon enough, and then I can do what I want with it."

The next morning, the king admired the beautiful ladies that the two fellows had brought. Then he said, "Now, Ti-Jean, what about you?"

"Oh, Ti-Jean, he's only got a great big white cat to show."

"Nevertheless," said the king, "I must see it."

Ti-Jean went and brought forth the cat. She had turned into a princess. The king was very surprised. She was so beautiful that he couldn't take his eyes off her. Then Ti-Jean went out and brought in the toads, and they were four of the most beautiful horses the king had ever seen.

"Well, Ti-Jean, you are the winner," said the king. He took the crown off his head and placed it on the head of Ti-Jean. Ti-Jean married the beautiful princess and that wedding was celebrated for days, far and near.

HALIBUT MAN AND THE HOUSE ON THE WAVES

retold by Dorothy de Wit

In the first days, in a village at the head of the Nass River, the people were starving. Raven was hungry, too, for no fish swam in the rivers, and the fish in the sea stayed so far from shore that the fishermen could not catch them. It was said that far out in the ocean there floated a huge house, the Abundant House, in which all the herring, the salmon, and the halibut were kept captive. But where it was, and how to find it, no one knew. Raven resolved to find the house, and one morning he set forth early and flew far to the west.

Hour after hour he flew, and finally, he saw far below him

something that looked like a large animal. Gulls circled around it, screaming into the wind. Down Raven dived, and he saw that the something was a huge cedar house, with a wide doorway. He settled silently on the roof and looked down the smoke hole. Below was a very big room, and sitting on the floor was a strange, thin man with a long head and silvery scales covering his body.

The man lifted a board in the floor, let down a line, and pulled up a large halibut. Then Raven knew that this was, indeed, the Abundant House, where lived Halibut Man, the keeper of all the herring, the salmon, and the halibut of the seas. Raven's mouth watered, and he began to devise a plan to take over the Abundant House.

First, he flew swiftly back to the village and called all the fishermen together. He told them to carve a harpoon, with a very long line. The fishermen made a harpoon, and for the line they tried the sinews of first one animal and then another. But each time they tested the line it broke. At last, the tomtit, a tiny grey wren, offered to lend them his sinews, which were known to be exceedingly tough.

Raven showed the women how to braid a line from the tomtit's sinews, as thin as a spider's web, long and very strong. Then the men fastened the harpoon firmly to a large sturdy canoe and waited. Raven's plan was to fly to the Abundant House and lure Halibut Man away. Then he would fly back toward the village, and when he came in sight of the canoe, he would wheel and rise straight up in the air. At this signal, the men were to follow his flight.

Across the water to the house on the waves raced Raven. Halibut Man was sitting on the floor of his house, looking out to sea when Raven appeared. Halibut Man looked surprised when the bird flew in the door, and he was even more surprised when Raven said, "At last, at last, I have found you, my brother! Our poor father told me to look everywhere, till I found you!"

"Who are you?" asked Halibut Man suspiciously.

"I am Raven-Who-Sets-Things-Right. Everyone knows me!"

"I do not know you, and I have never even heard your name!" retorted Halibut Man rudely.

"Then you are the first not to have heard of me!" replied Raven. "I brought the Box of Daylight from the Over-sky Country to the people. I stole fire and gave it to them. I found fresh water for them to drink. And I forced Tchanegoa, the Tide Woman, to hold back the waters of the sea each day, so that the people could gather mussels, and crabs, and clams for food."

But Halibut Man still looked at Raven coldly. "I have been a man and lived in this house since the beginning of the world. I have no father, no mother, no family, for I was created when the world was made. I am Halibut Man!"

"Ahhhhh, there you are wrong, my brother!" Raven spoke very earnestly. "Our father from the Over-sky Country lost you when you fell from there to the bottom of the sea! He has sent me in search of you, and I have flown everywhere, for he wishes to see his dear son again, after so long a time. Come with me, and I will take you to him. But first, I am very weary from flying, and I am terribly hungry!"

"Indeed, you must be hungry!" said Halibut Man. "I will feed

you." He opened the floorboard and let down his line. After a few minutes he hauled it in, and a large halibut flapped at its end. He cut up the halibut and put it to steam. While it was cooking, he turned to Raven, who had been examining the house and the smoke hole very carefully.

"You've made me wonder about my father. I would like to see if what you say is true. But I cannot fly, and I have no way of going to him."

Raven answered craftily, "Oh, that is no problem! I can carry you on my back. My wings are broad and very strong."

"Yes, but I am of the sea and have never travelled through the air. Suppose I should fall off! I might be killed!" Halibut Man shuddered at the thought but looked somewhat relieved at Raven's reply.

"Oh, you needn't worry. Your house is very large. Before we leave, I'll take you on my back and fly around in here so you can practise holding on. It is very safe. You will like flying!"

Halibut Man climbed onto Raven's back, though somewhat fearfully. Raven flew about slowly and stayed close to the floor at first. But when he felt that Halibut Man sat securely on him, he mounted up to the smoke hole and flew out to sea.

"Sit firmly, Halibut Man," he called. "I am going to fly higher, toward the land where your father awaits you." And he flew farther and farther away from the Abundant House.

Then suddenly he flipped over and flew upside down! Down, down, down plunged Halibut Man into the cold waves. Raven righted himself and laughed! Now he could fly back to the villagers and the waiting fishermen.

But first, he would go back and gobble up the delicious halibut that was steaming in the house on the waves. When Raven had eaten the halibut, he was hungry for another. He decided to catch one through the hole in the floor in the same way as Halibut Man had done. So he let down the line and croaked loudly in anticipation when he felt a bite.

But his croak stopped in midair as he drew up the line. Clutching it with both hands was Halibut Man! His fish eyes glared as he

grabbed Raven's neck and twisted it.

"That will silence your lying tongue for good. Did you really think you could get rid of me by dropping me into the water when I can live in the sea anywhere as well as in my own house?"

Raven drifted on the waves, still, and apparently lifeless. The tide carried him landward and finally washed him ashore near his own village.

But Raven, though hurting all over, was by no means dead! As soon as he felt the sand under him, he lay there to rest for a while, then shook himself and spoke to the fishermen. "I will fly on a straight course to the Abundant House of Halibut Man. Follow me with the harpoon, and when you see me fly down to the roof, aim it at the house. Then—all of you—begin to sing. Sing loudly, and pull, pull, with all your might!"

Raven flew, straight as a dart, to the Abundant House, and when he landed, the fishermen threw the harpoon, with its tomtit line. The great hook buried itself in the wood of the house, and the

wind snatched up the line and wrapped it around the building. Raven, on the roof, flapped his wings. The line grew taut as it began to pull the great structure toward the shore, slowly at first, then faster and faster, as it was caught by the current.

The singing of the fishermen grew louder and louder as they neared the shore. Suddenly the door flew open, and Halibut Man leaped into the sea, where he swam deep below to the Kingdom Under the Waves.

And after him spilled forth a flood of herring, and salmon, and halibut, and oolachen!

"From now on," croaked Raven to the villagers, "all the fish of the sea are yours, and you need hunger no longer!"

The people sang and sang, till the songs filled the air, and the fish surged through the sea and up the rivers, for all the days to come.

And even now the villagers sing these same songs when it is the fishing season along the Nass River.

THE FISH OF THE SEA

Traditional

Come, all you young sailormen, listen to me,
I'll sing you a song of the fish of the sea,

And it's windy weather, boys, stormy weather, boys,
When the wind blows, we're all together, boys,
Blow ye winds westerly, blow ye winds blow,
Jolly sou'wester, boys, steady she goes.

Up jumps the eel with his slippery tail,
Climbs up aloft and reefs the topsail,

Then up jumps the shark with his nine rows of teeth,
Saying, "You eat the dough, boys, and I'll eat the beef."

Up jumps the lobster with his heavy claws,
Bites the main boom right off by the jaws,

    Up jumps the halibut, lies flat on the deck,
    He says, "Mr. Captain, don't step on my neck!"

Up jumps the herring, the king of the sea,
Saying, "All other fishes, now you follow me!"

    Up jumps the codfish with his chuckle-head,
    He runs out up forward and throws out the lead,

Up jumps the whale, the largest of all,
"If you want any wind, well I'll blow ye a squall!"

    And it's windy weather, boys, stormy weather, boys,
    When the wind blows, we're all together, boys,
    Blow ye winds westerly, blow ye winds blow,
    Jolly sou'wester, boys, steady she goes.

THE WILL

by Ian Serraillier

There was an old man who had three sons
And seventeen horses. "I've written my will,"
He told his sons. "I'm going to leave
My horses to the three of you,
But you must share them as I say."

The old man died. The will was opened:
"To my three sons I leave
My seventeen horses.
My eldest son shall take half;
My second son shall take a third;
My youngest son shall take a ninth.

Shed no blood,
Do not kill;
You must obey
Your father's will."

The three sons were puzzled. At school
They'd been well taught, but not so well
That they could divide
    17 by 2,
        17 by 3,
            17 by 9,
And still obey their father's will.

What did they do?

They went to a wise man and asked
His advice. "I will give you a horse,"
Said the wise man. "Now go away
And obey your father's will."

They took the horse and went away.

They now had eighteen horses.
The eldest son took half;
The second son took a third;
The youngest son took a ninth.
And the wise man's horse? They gave it back.

Why did the old man write his will like that?

THE WINTER WREN

by Brock Cole

O ne year spring would not come.

The new wheat turned yellow and rotted in the furrows, and in the air was a taste of iron.

There was little to eat in the village, and so when Simon burned the porridge and spilled the milk, his mother was very angry.

"You daft thing!" she cried. "Can't you do anything right?"

Simon scratched his head and thought, but he couldn't be sure. "Don't be sad, Mother," he said, "You'll think of something."

His mother sighed and shook her head. "Well, why don't you climb up on the barn and watch for spring? Perhaps you can do that right." And it will keep him out of harm's way, she thought.

"But what does she look like?"

"Who?"

"Why, Spring!"

"Oh, you are a sweet befuddling fool!" And his mother laughed in spite of herself. "She must be a princess all dressed in green and gold."

But when Simon got to the top of the barn there wasn't a sign of a princess in green and gold. All that he saw were two ravens fighting over a bit of bacon rind.

"Give me a bite," begged one, "and when Spring comes, I'll find you a nice robin's egg."

"That will be never," said the other, laughing. "Spring's asleep at Winter's farm and can't wake up."

With a snip and a snap of his great bill, he swallowed the bacon and flew away.

"So that's the way it is," said Simon, and he slid down the thatch and went to tell his mother.

"Goodbye, Mother. You'll have to manage without me for a while. There's nothing else for it."

"Where are you going?" she asked.

"Why, haven't you heard? Spring's asleep at Winter's farm and can't wake up, poor thing. I'm going to help her."

"Take me with you," said his sister Meg.

Who could say no to little Meg?

Not Simon.

Their mother didn't know what to make of such foolishness, but

she gave them a small sack of meal and an apple in case they got hungry, and a kiss each for her little daughter and her great daft son.

"How will we know Spring when we find her?" asked Meg.

"She's a princess all dressed in green and gold, that's for sure," said Simon.

"Oh," said Meg, and was quiet.

With Meg on his back, Simon walked and walked, but he didn't get tired. His sister weighed hardly more than a bird.

Finally they came to a farm where nothing grew.

There was Winter, striding back and forth over his fields, sowing the earth with sleet.

"Hey, Old Winter!" called Simon. "Where is Spring? We've come to wake her up!"

But Winter would have none of that. He gave a great roar and threw a handful of ice at the two children.

Simon turned to run. Quick as he was, he was not quick enough. A hailstone hit Meg smack in the back.

There was a pop and a twitter, and Meg disappeared.

Where she had been was nothing but a tiny brown winter wren, who flew up in a tree over Simon's head.

Poor Simon sat down and began to cry.

"Don't cry, Simon," said the Winter Wren, and she flew down and sat by his shoulder. "Do as I say, and everything will come right."

Simon wiped his eyes and blew his nose. "What shall I do, Winter Wren?" he asked.

"Creep up close behind Winter, and where he sows sleet, you sow meal."

Simon did as the Winter Wren said. Wherever Winter sowed sleet, Simon spread a bit of meal from the sack that his mother had given him.

And wherever a speck of meal fell, there sprang up a fresh green stalk of wheat.

The green spikes prickled and tickled Old Winter's toes so that he danced and stamped.

"Who sows meal where I sow sleet?" he cried, twisting this way and that. But Simon kept close to Winter's back so that he couldn't be seen.

It was too much for Winter. He threw down his sack of sleet and stomped off over the fields.

"After him quickly!" cried the Winter Wren, and Simon ran as fast as he could.

Soon he saw Winter again, pruning the buds from his apple trees.

"Creep up close," whispered the Winter Wren, "and throw your apple into the orchard."

Simon did as the Winter Wren said, and where his apple touched the ground a great tree sprang up and blossomed.

When Winter touched the tree, his sickle melted, and his cold fingers burned.

"Who plants where I prune?" he cried, and turned this way and that. But Simon hid beneath the blowing blossoms, and Winter couldn't find him.

The old fellow growled and bellowed and fled into his house.

"After him quickly!" called the Winter Wren.

But the door was locked fast, and Simon could not open it.

"Blow through the keyhole," said the Winter Wren.

Simon did as he was told, and his warm breath melted the locks quite away, for Winter's locks are nothing but ice.

The door sprang open, but there was no sign of Winter. In all of his cold kitchen there was no one but a little girl spreading butter on a piece of bread.

"Hello. I've come to wake up Spring," said Simon.

"You have?" said the girl. "And will you know her when you see her?"

"Oh yes. She's a princess all dressed in green and gold."

"A princess in green and gold? That would be at the top of the stairs," said the girl, and took her breakfast into the garden.

As Simon went up the stairs he could hear the Winter Wren singing overhead, but when he reached the landing the singing stopped.

In a tiny bedroom filled with flowers was a great feather bed, and on the feather bed someone sat up and yawned.

Was it Spring?

No. It was Meg.

"Oh, Meg, there you are," said Simon, picking up his sister and giving her a hug. "But where is Spring?"

A warm wind shook the curtains and made the windows clatter, and Simon looked out.

"So that's the way it is!" he said, laughing. "Look, Meg. There she is. Wide awake now."

Down they went, out into Winter's garden, and started across the fields for home.

Spring rolled before them like a great green wave.

When they reached their village, their mother and the other villagers were planting lettuce and potatoes.

"Spring came while you were gone, Simon," said his mother.

"I know. We woke her up at Winter's farm."

"You did, did you?" said his mother, laughing. "And was she a princess all dressed in green and gold?"

"Oh no, you were quite wrong about that," said Simon. "She was nothing but a bit of a girl, just like our Meg." And he sat his sister up on a wagon so that everyone could see just how Spring was.

The villagers all laughed, but Simon's mother gave him a hug, because she loved him even if he was a sweet befuddling fool.

The Flying Horse Machine

retold by Barbara Winther

Scene 1

SETTING: *King Sabur's palace courtyard, in ancient Persia.*

CURTAIN OPENS: **KING SABUR** *is seated on throne,* 1ST GUARD, *stands beside him.* **PRINCE KAMAR**, *with a sword at his side, and* **PRINCESS FAHAN**, *stand together, talking.*

KAMAR: The festival of Nau-Roz is almost over, sister Princess Fahan. I am impressed with the marvellous inventions entered in Father's annual contest. Which would you choose as the best?

FAHAN: M-m-m. Well, brother Prince Kamar, I believe I prefer the golden peacock that can tell the time of day.

KAMAR: It is beautiful, but what about the mechanical guard made of precious gems that holds a silver trumpet? Whenever an enemy approaches, the figure blows a fierce warning. Think of how beneficial it would be in ruling Persia. That is always Father's first concern.

FAHAN: Yes, perhaps you are right. However, Father has not yet declared the winner. Last year the prize was given by noon. Now it is almost evening, and his mind is still not made up. (*Commotion is heard offstage.* 2ND GUARD *enters and falls on knees before* KING.)

2ND GUARD: King Sabur, sublime Sultan of Persia, an old man seeks admittance to demonstrate his invention.

KING (*eagerly*): Send him in at once. (2ND GUARD *exits.*) Strange. All afternoon I have felt it necessary to wait for one more contestant. (MAROUDAH, *the magician, enters, followed by* 2ND GUARD.)

MAROUDAH (*bowing*): King Sabur, I am Maroudah, the magnificent magician. I have invented a miraculous magic horse machine. (FLYING HORSE MACHINE *enters, snorting and neighing. A large key and removable knob are on horse's head.* HORSE *is followed by curious court* ATTENDANTS.)

KING (*thoughtfully*): Your horse machine is interesting, Maroudah, but there have been more remarkable inventions here today.

MAROUDAH: Ah, but you have not seen what my invention will do. This, great Sultan, is a flying horse machine.

ALL (*amazed*): A flying horse machine?

KING: Demonstrate that what you say is true.

MAROUDAH: With pleasure. (*Climbs onto* HORSE *and turns key.* HORSE *paws ground, neighs, and exits. All look upward, point, gasp, as they pantomime watching* HORSE *flying overhead.*)

ALL: Look! The horse is flying! See how it soars! (*They pantomime watching* HORSE *descend and finally land. In a moment* HORSE, *with* MAROUDAH *riding it, re-enters.*) Amazing! Wonderful! Fantastic! Surely this invention will win the prize.

KING (*rising, holding up hands for quiet*): Never have I beheld such a marvel. What possibilities this horse machine has for me! Every day I could fly above my kingdom. In a moment I could find anyone. I could visit the farthest city. I could spy on my enemies. I could cast fear into the hearts of entire armies.

Maroudah, I declare you the winner of the Nau-Roz Festival Contest. Name your prize. Anything you desire shall be yours. Anything.

MAROUDAH: My prize, King Sabur, will be to marry your daughter, Princess Fahan. (FAHAN *gasps and backs away.* KING *is astonished.* KAMAR *steps forward to protest. Others are alarmed.*)

FAHAN: No! Please, Father, do not make me marry him.

KING: I am sorry, my daughter. I have given my word. A king cannot go back on a promise.

KAMAR: Although I have the highest respect for you, Father, I am shocked that you would force my sister, your obedient and gentle daughter, to marry this ugly and evil wizard.

MAROUDAH (*angrily*): Prince Kamar, though your words are sharp arrows, they fall only on parched desert sands. Princess Fahan is mine. I have won her fairly in exchange for this flying horse machine.

KAMAR: It may be a trick, Father. The horse may fly only when Maroudah rides it. The machine may have no value to anyone else.

KING: Maroudah, how can I be certain the horse will fly without you?

MAROUDAH: Try it, sire. But, no, since it is Prince Kamar who does not believe, he should be the one to test the horse.

KAMAR: I am eager to do so, for I feel this magician hides truth to gain his desire. (*Climbs onto* HORSE)

MAROUDAH (*indicating key*): There is the key to make the machine go up. (KAMAR *quickly exits on* HORSE. *As before, all pantomime watching* HORSE *fly across stage.*)

ALL: Prince Kamar flies higher and higher.

FAHAN (*crying out*): Brother, brother, come back!

KING: Maroudah, why doesn't he come down?

MAROUDAH (*laughing*): Because he does not know how. I did not show him the secret knob for downward flight. He will probably fly into the sun before he can find the knob.

KING: You did this deliberately!

MAROUDAH: Yes, Prince Kamar tried to interfere with my plans. And now—(*yanks* FAHAN *toward him*) Now I have Princess Fahan. (FAHAN *struggles and cries out.*)

KING (*yelling*): Guards, guards, seize him! (GUARDS *rush toward* MAROUDAH, *who exits in a flash of light, pulling* FAHAN *behind him.* GUARDS *stagger back and fall as if stunned. Others shriek in fear.*)

ALL: Where are they? The princess has been kidnapped.

KING: Kamar, search for the secret knob. Fahan, it is my fault you have been spirited away. My greedy desire to own the flying horse machine has cost me my children. (*Curtain closes.*)

SCENE 2

BEFORE CURTAIN OPENS: KAMAR *enters leading* HORSE.

KAMAR: I was almost to the sun before I found the secret knob to direct the horse downward. I have landed on a green island—I know not where—the roof I stand on is golden, the highest point of a walled city. Perhaps, inside this noble palace I shall find someone to help me. (KAMAR *exits with* HORSE. *Curtain opens.*)

SETTING: *Princess Shamour's room in the golden palace of Ceylon.*

CURTAIN OPENS: PRINCESS SHAMOUR *is resting on couch, leaning on one elbow, and watching* ATTENDANTS *dance to Indian music.* KAMAR *enters through window. Music stops.* ATTENDANTS, *seeing him, muffle screams and run fearfully downstage, huddling in a group.* PRINCESS SHAMOUR *rises and turns away in alarm.*

KAMAR: Wait, please. Lovely lady, I mean you no harm. (*She stops and turns to look at him. They stare at each other, frozen for a moment, then speak as if enchanted.*)

SHAMOUR: Who are you?

KAMAR: Prince Kamar of Persia. And your name?

SHAMOUR: Shamour, Princess of Ceylon.

KAMAR: I am charmed by your grace and beauty.

SHAMOUR: Thank you, handsome Prince. But how did you come to our island kingdom? I am certain our guards would have seen a ship arrive and spread the alarm.

KAMAR: I flew here. (*All gasp.*)

SHAMOUR: What powers you must possess! Are you part god, or do you cast spells in league with dark spirits?

KAMAR: Neither, Princess Shamour. I flew here on a horse machine invented by the magician, Maroudah.

SHAMOUR: Maroudah! I know that cruel man.

KAMAR: Indeed he is evil. He tried to kill me, but I learned his secret just in time and escaped.

SHAMOUR: Few escape his clutches. I, too, was lucky enough to save myself from him. It is said that Maroudah has a palace in India, hidden in a valley between two mountains. It is guarded by a fierce giant bird called a Roc. Each year the magician steals a new princess and carries her to that palace. Once he almost captured me, but I pretended to be insane and he quickly disappeared, for Maroudah fears madness more than anything.

KAMAR: If only my sister had known that! I am afraid he may have captured her.

SHAMOUR: Since you have the horse machine, let us fly to the hidden palace to see if it be true.

KAMAR: Yes, I will fly there, but alone. I have imposed too much on your kindness.

SHAMOUR: Let me go with you to help.

KAMAR: No, I would not have you risk any more danger. But I will return, lovely princess, to be your suitor, and if I find favour in your eyes, I will ask your father for your hand in marriage. For in all the world there is no other I would want for my wife.

SHAMOUR: May Buddha protect you and bring you safely back. (*He exits.*)

ATTENDANTS (*excitedly*): How handsome he is! Prince of Persia. See how the horse flies over the water!

SHAMOUR: I fear for them. Come, please, entertain me, for I am uneasy. (*Indian music is heard and* ATTENDANTS *dance as at beginning of scene, while* SHAMOUR *returns to rest on couch. Curtain slowly closes.*)

SCENE 3

BEFORE CURTAIN OPENS: **KAMAR** *enters, leading horse.*

KAMAR: This is the valley the Princess described. And there is the palace! (**ROC** *enters from behind* **KAMAR** *and rushes toward him, flapping wings and screeching fiercely.* **KAMAR** *turns quickly, draws sword, and battles with* **ROC**, *who uses wings, beak, and talons to combat* **KAMAR***'s sword, all the while making frightening noises. Finally* **KAMAR** *manages to wound* **ROC**, *who staggers about, then howling mournfully, flies away.* **FAHAN** *immediately enters, running toward* **KAMAR**.)

FAHAN: Brother Prince Kamar! Praise be to Allah, you have rescued me and killed the Roc.

KAMAR: My sister, you are alive! Maroudah, where is he?

FAHAN: He has returned to Persia.

KAMAR: Why so?

FAHAN: Because I would have nothing to do with Maroudah and his orders, that miserable magician plans to torture Father before my eyes until I meet his demands.

KAMAR: The fiend! Quickly, onto the flying horse machine! First we will stop on the island of Ceylon. Then we will return to Persia to confront Maroudah and try to thwart his plans. (*All exit. Curtain opens.*)

SETTING: *Same as Scene 1.*

CURTAIN OPENS: **KING** *is seated on throne, head in hands.* **1ST GUARD**, *stands beside him, also looking unhappy.* **ATTENDANTS** *stand, talking in hushed tones.*

1ST ATTENDANT: King Sabur has not eaten for days.

2ND ATTENDANT: The people of Persia are wondering if they still have a king.

3RD ATTENDANT: He has been this way ever since the loss of his son and daughter. I fear for our country. (*Voices are heard offstage.* **2ND GUARD** *enters, running, and falls to knees before* **KING**.)

2ND GUARD: King Sabur, sublime Sultan of Persia, Maroudah the magician has come back. (*All gasp.* **KING** *leaps to feet.* **1ST GUARD**

rushes forward. **KING** *waves him back.*)

KING: No, wait, guard. Only Maroudah knows where Princess Fahan is hidden. (*To* **2ND GUARD**) Show the wizard into the courtyard, and, for now, be most courteous.

2ND GUARD (*rising*): Yes, King Sabur. (*Exits, immediately re-entering and making elaborate bow to present* **MAROUDAH**. **2ND GUARD** *exits.*)

MAROUDAH (*bowing*): We meet again, King Sabur.

KING: Where is my daughter?

MAROUDAH: In India, sire. At my secret palace, living in magnificent splendour.

KING: Bring her here at once, or I will have your head cut off.

MAROUDAH: If you take my head, you will lose your daughter.

KING: Why have you come here, Maroudah?

MAROUDAH: Because your daughter is homesick. She misses her father and begs me to ask that you pay her a visit. Will you accompany me back to my palace so your daughter will be even happier than she is now?

KING: Yes, I shall go with you. (*Whispers to* **1ST GUARD**, *who nods.*)

MAROUDAH: King Sabur, you must come *alone.*

KING: The King of Persia goes nowhere without guards.

MAROUDAH: If you wish to see your daughter, you will come by yourself.

KING (*with resignation*): All right, Maroudah. You win. I shall go alone with you. Lead the way. (*Commotion is heard offstage.* **2ND GUARD** *re-enters, waving his arms.*) What is it, Guard?

2ND GUARD: King Sabur! King Sabur! Your son and daughter— they are here!

MAROUDAH: What? Impossible! (**KAMAR, FAHAN** *and* **PRINCESS SHAMOUR** *enter and bow.* **KING** *embraces his children.*)

KING: This is the happiest moment of my life. Both my children have returned safely to my kingdom. My prayers to Allah have been answered. And who is this lady?

KAMAR: Father, I present Princess Shamour of Ceylon. Her father has agreed to our marriage. All we need is your blessing.

KING: You have it, my son. But before we speak of the wedding, tell me, what has happened. How did you find your sister?

KAMAR: With the help of Princess Shamour and by riding the flying horse machine. (**HORSE** *enters.*)

ALL: The flying horse machine. The Prince must have found the secret knob. (*Suddenly* **MAROUDAH** *leaps forward.*)

MAROUDAH: Prince Kamar, you have outwitted me, but you shall pay for it. You will all pay. I shall cast an evil spell on everyone in this palace.

SHAMOUR (*aside to* **KAMAR**):   Remember, insanity is what the magician fears most. (**KAMAR** *nods and, to everyone's astonishment, drops to hands and knees and begins meowing like a cat.* **SHAMOUR** *also drops to hands and knees and begins barking like a dog, chasing* **KAMAR** *in a circle around* **MAROUDAH**. *They start leaping into the air with crazy laughs and weird motions, frightening* **MAROUDAH**.)

KING: What has happened? My poor son and daughter-to-be have lost their minds. What a terrible homecoming! (*Falls to his knees, wailing, as do* **ATTENDANTS**, **GUARDS** *and* **FAHAN**. **MAROUDAH**, *biting his nails nervously, tiptoes to* **HORSE** *and climbs onto it.*)

MAROUDAH: I must leave quickly before I catch their madness. (*Laughing, he turns key and exits on* **HORSE**. **SHAMOUR** *and* **KAMAR** *rise and hold up arms for silence.*)

KAMAR: Do not worry. We are perfectly sane.

SHAMOUR: We acted that way to frighten away the magician.

FAHAN: Look, there he goes, flying into the sky. (*Others rise and pantomime watching him fly overhead.*)

KING: I fear he will come back to bring more trouble to my kingdom.

KAMAR: He will not return, Father. (*Takes knob out of pocket and holds it up*) I took off the secret knob which makes the horse fly down. It will fly up and up, into the sky, until it is consumed by the flames of the sun. It is fitting that Maroudah, the evil magician, will be destroyed by his own magic machine. (*Curtain closes.*)

RHYMES OF OLD

Granfa' Grig had a pig,
In a field of clover;
Piggie died, Granfa' cried,
And all the fun was over.

A little pig found a fifty-dollar note,
And purchased a hat and a very fine coat,
With trousers, and stockings, and shoes,
Cravat, and shirt-collar, and gold-headed cane;
Then, proud as could be, did he march up the lane;
Says he, "I shall hear all the news."

Higglety, pigglety, pop!
The dog has eaten the mop;
The pig's in a hurry,
The cat's in a flurry,
Higglety, pigglety, pop!

Here I am, little jumping Joan;
When nobody's with me,
I'm all alone.

Grey goose and gander,
Waft your wings together,
And carry the good king's daughter
Over the one-strand river.

A wise old owl lived in an oak;
The more he saw the less he spoke;
The less he spoke the more he heard.
Why aren't we all like that wise old bird?

Doctor Foster went to Glo'ster
In a shower of rain.
He stepped in a puddle,
Right up to his middle,
And never went there again.

If I had as much money as I could spend,
I never would cry old chairs to mend;
Old chairs to mend, old chairs to mend,
I never would cry old chairs to mend;

If I had as much money as I could tell,
I never would cry old clothes to sell;
Old clothes to sell, old clothes to sell,
I never would cry old clothes to sell.

LIKE ALL THE OTHERS

Have you ever heard parents or grandparents talk about where they lived when they were young? Perhaps they lived in a different town or even another country. Did they live in an apartment, or a house in the country, or even a log cabin? People live in all kinds of dwellings all over the world, but to each family, their home is special. It protects them from the weather and from danger, and there they share their lives with people they love. Is this house like yours?

Our house, like all the others in Orchid Grove, had a living room and a scullery and two bedrooms. Our back bedroom was in a bad state because the roof needed repairing, so we four children

all slept downstairs in the living room. We had a big iron bedstead, and Harold and I slept with our heads at one end and Sandra and Jean at the other. There was room for all of us, and we had some blankets and old coats to keep us warm, and it was a very good arrangement.

(from *Trouble in the Jungle*, by John Rowe Townsend)

Families make their homes, and then several homes grow into a community. The selections in this section talk about different homes in different places; perhaps you will be able to find your home or your community in one of these stories.

OLD MACDONALD HAD AN APARTMENT HOUSE

by Judith Barrett

Old MacDonald lived in a big apartment house with his wife and their dog. He didn't own the building. Fat Mr. Wrental did. Old MacDonald was its Super.

He polished the brass doorknobs when they got smudgy, mopped up the hallways when they got dirty, and sent up steam when it got cold.

Old MacDonald's apartment was on the bottom floor and was very dark.

The windows were covered by a thick bushy hedge that grew in the front yard.

Without sunlight, his wife's tomato plant grew pale and droopy.

So, Old MacDonald decided to cut down the hedge in front of the windows.

With all the sunlight that came in, the plant straightened up, grew a few leaves, and even grew a few tomatoes.

But, the spot where the hedge had been looked very empty, so Old MacDonald's wife suggested that they fill it with her tomato plant. And they did.

It grew lots of new leaves, many more tomatoes, and much, much taller.

"Why not get rid of all the rest of the hedge." Old MacDonald said. "Then instead I could plant vegetables in the yard. They're better looking than the hedge and much better tasting, too." So he cut the whole hedge down to the ground and in its place he planted rows of corn and melons and beans and radishes. The fountain became a self-watering pea patch. The front yard had become a small farm and the tenants were amazed.

One of the tenants, Mrs. Katz, really didn't need four rooms anymore.

Her children were grown up. So, she moved out.

It occurred to Old MacDonald then that an empty apartment would be a good place to grow lots more vegetables. He quickly moved in some soil and proceeded to redecorate in Late Vegetarian style. He laid down a carpet of carrots and cabbages, put some sweet potatoes where the couch had been, and stuffed the closet with mushrooms.

Some days later, Mrs. Katz's downstairs neighbour, Mr. Hopkins, turned on a faucet and got hot and cold running sweet potato vines. Above his head he could see carrots popping through the ceiling. He became furious. "Either that garden up there goes or I go," he screamed at Old MacDonald.

But Old MacDonald really didn't care. He had begun to feel that in some ways vegetables made better tenants than people. Carrots didn't smudge brass doorknobs. Cucumbers didn't leave muddy footprints in the halls. And potatoes didn't bang on the radiators for more steam.

Angry Mr. Hopkins moved out. A variety of vegetables, a field of clover, and a cow moved in.

No one knew what Old MacDonald was doing, but you can't keep a cow a secret for very long.

More and more people moved out, very disgusted with what was happening.

So more vegetables, fruit trees, cows, and chickens took their place.

Finally every tenant in the building had moved out. The apartment house became a four-storey barn.

Then one day Fat Mr. Wrental, the owner, stopped by to check on the house and collect the rent money as he did every few months. When he saw that his tenants had been replaced by vegetables, fruit trees, cows, and chickens, he got upset. Very upset.

"Look here, Old MacDonald, what have you done?" he shouted. "Where are the families? All that's here now are bushels of fruits and vegetables, herds of cows, and flocks of chickens. And they can't pay me rent."

Old MacDonald and his wife were very sad. They knew they would have to leave. Fat Mr. Wrental told them so. In fact, he was going to have the whole farm thrown out into the street.

Old MacDonald told his wife not to cry near her tomato plant because the salt water wouldn't be good for it.

Besides, it set a bad example for the cows.

Fat Mr. Wrental paced back and forth quickly in front of the house. He was very upset and not really sure that he liked the idea of throwing the farm out into the street. Old MacDonald had been such a good Super. Now not only was he without tenants, but he'd be without a Super, too.

"Who ever heard of a farm in the middle of the city? That's absurd," he muttered. "Or is it? Maybe a farm could pay me rent after all."

The next morning Old MacDonald and his wife stepped outside the house carrying their suitcases, and in the middle of the front walk Fat Mr. Wrental was building a store. There was a big sign

that read "Wrental and MacDonald's Fruits and Vegetables—Fresh Milk and Eggs Hourly."

Fat Mr. Wrental waved at Old MacDonald and shouted, "Where are you going, partner? You grow the stuff, and I'll sell it. Vegetables will pay me rent after all."

On opening day the store was jammed. Fat Mr. Wrental made a very long speech in which he asked everyone to come in very often and to buy as much as they could.

He asked Old MacDonald to say a few words, and he did. He said "People, I am happy to have such fine vegetables as tenants. I hope you agree that good vegetables make good neighbours."

The people applauded and then began to buy as much as they could. They came back day after day.

Both the store and the farm thrived throughout the summer and fall. And even in winter, when the earth outside was frozen and covered with snow, things were still growing on the steam-heated farm.

THE RAINBOW CONNECTION

by Paul Williams and Kenny Ascher

Why are there so many songs about rainbows,
and what's on the other side?
Rainbows are visions, but only illusions,
And rainbows have nothing to hide.
So we've been told, and some chose to believe it;
I know they're wrong, wait and see.

> Someday we'll find it, the Rainbow Connection;
> The lovers, the dreamers, and me.

Who said that ev'ry wish would be heard and answered
when wished on the morning star?
Somebody thought of that, and someone believed it;
look what it's done so far.
What's so amazing that keeps us star-gazing,
And what do we think we might see?

> Someday we'll find it, the Rainbow Connection;
> The lovers, the dreamers, and me.

Have you been half asleep and have you heard voices?
I've heard them calling my name.
Is this the sweet sound that calls the young sailors?
The voice might be one and the same.
I've heard it too many times to ignore it.
It's something that I'm s'posed to be.

Someday we'll find it, the Rainbow Connection;
The lovers, the dreamers, and me.

WHEN I WAS YOUNG
IN THE MOUNTAINS

by Cynthia Rylant

When I was young in the mountains,
Grandfather came home in the evening
covered with the black dust of a coal mine.
Only his lips were clean, and he used them
to kiss the top of my head.

When I was young in the mountains,
Grandmother spread the table with hot
corn bread, pinto beans and fried okra.
Later, in the middle of the night,
she walked through the grass with me to the
johnny-house and held my hand in the dark.
I promised never to eat more than one serving
of okra again.

When I was young in the mountains,
we walked across the cow pasture and through
the woods, carrying our towels. The swimming
hole was dark and muddy, and we sometimes
saw snakes, but we jumped in anyway.
On our way home, we stopped at
Mr. Crawford's for a mound of white butter.
Mr. Crawford and Mrs. Crawford looked
alike and always smelled of sweet milk.

When I was young in the mountains,
we pumped pails of water from the well at
the bottom of the hill, and heated the water
to fill round tin tubs for our baths.
Afterward we stood in front of the
old black stove, shivering and giggling,
while Grandmother heated cocoa on top.

When I was young in the mountains,
we went to church in the schoolhouse
on Sundays, and sometimes walked with the
congregation through the cow pasture
to the dark swimming hole, for baptisms.
My cousin Peter was laid back into the
water, and his white shirt stuck to him,
and my Grandmother cried.

When I was young in the mountains,
we listened to frogs sing at dusk and awoke
to cowbells outside our windows. Sometimes
a black snake came in the yard, and my
Grandmother would threaten it with a hoe.
If it did not leave, she used the hoe
to kill it. Four of us once draped a very
long snake, dead of course, across our necks
for a photograph.

When I was young in the mountains,
we sat on the porch swing in the evenings,
and Grandfather sharpened my pencils with his
pocketknife. Grandmother sometimes shelled
beans and sometimes braided my hair. The dogs
lay around us, and the stars sparkled in the sky.
A bobwhite whistled in the forest.
Bob-bob-bobwhite!

When I was young in the mountains,
I never wanted to go to the ocean, and I never
wanted to go to the desert. I never wanted
to go anywhere else in the world, for I was
in the mountains. And that was always enough.

A Revolving Door

A revolving door
swallows
crowds of people

then
spits them out
packaged in singles
  one
    by
  one
    by
  one
    by
  one

Storm Over Lake Ontario

Lightning
a sky zipper
zipping
the blue black sky
in two
shooting
sparkling fire
zig-zagging
across
the black ink lake
spotlighting
angry waves
hammering
the fiery beach

Street Action

Jackhammers, sledge hammers
shovels and picks
pile drivers, back hoes
gravel trucks and cranes
cement-chomping jaws
gobble up sidewalks
asphalt and trees
shake all the buildings   then
topple brick chimneys   dig up the street
crack plaster walls   bury water pipes
     fill up the holes

tunnel to China
bury dinosaur pipes   dig up the street
     bury telephone cables
add sand and gravel   fill up the holes
and smelly tar mix

     dig up the street
muscles and sweat   bury hydro lines
     fill up the holes

a smooth city street

     city streets are
     adult sand piles

Poems by Lola Sneyd

HOME

by Douglas Young

Every day, all over the world, billions of people start and end their day at home. Home is probably the most important place in most people's lives.

What do homes do for us? One of the most important things they do is protect us from unpleasant weather outside. They keep us dry when it's wet outside, warm when it's cold, and cool when it's hot. We are unhappy with our home if the roof leaks and lets in the rain, or if the fire or furnace goes out in the middle of the night and we feel cold in the morning when we wake up.

Another important thing that homes do is provide us with a place to make and eat meals and a place to sleep at night. We obviously could not live without eating and sleeping. Eating in restaurants can be fun, but after a few such meals most people start to miss "home-cooked" food. In the same way many people think their bed at home is the most comfortable bed in the world and can't sleep well anywhere else.

All sorts of places can be considered homes—tents, huts, caves, boats, trailers, houses, or big apartment buildings. Though such places look very different, they all have some things in common.

The same four ingredients are required to make a home anywhere in the world: space, building materials, labour, and money. The space (land or water) is needed because it is where the house will be built. The building materials (wood, canvas, animal skins, brick, steel) are what the dwelling is made of. The labour is the work of the men and women (carpenters, plumbers, bricklayers, electricians) who will build the home. The money is needed to pay for the other three.

While homes everywhere have these ingredients in common, and while they all have walls, floors, and roofs, they do look different from one part of the world to another. For example, a house in Canada looks very unlike one in West Africa or China. One of the principal reasons for this is climate. A house built in an area with long, cold winters and heavy snowfalls will look different from one built in a tropical climate where it is hot every day of the year.

The cold climate dwelling will have a roof with a pitch or a slope to shed snow so the roof will not collapse under the weight of the snow. It will also have a heating system to keep the air (and the people) inside the house warm. To make sure the warm air stays inside and the cold air stays outside, windows and doors will be small and must shut tightly.

The warm climate dwelling needs little or no heating system because the weather seldom gets cold. Windows and doors may always be left open to let a cooling breeze blow through the house. In some hot countries homes are lifted off the ground on columns to allow cool breezes to blow under them. In countries that are very hot, homes must keep the sun out at all times; otherwise the inside of the house will become uncomfortably warm. Homes in such countries will have very small windows and dark, cool interiors.

Another reason why homes in various parts of the world look different is the building materials that are available. For example, in countries such as Canada and Sweden, there is plenty of wood and, as a result, a lot of homes are built mostly of wood. In countries that don't have large forests people must build their homes out of something else—usually bricks made from clay, mud, or cement. What building materials is your home made from?

In times past many people built their own homes, but most likely you and your family live in a house or apartment that was built by a builder. A good home should "fit" your family just like a glove fits your hand or a shoe fits your foot. If you had all the money in the world and built your own home, it would probably fit very well. You probably live in a home that was built by someone who never met your family. Does it fit you?

In many parts of the world people still build their own homes because they are too poor to buy them. For example, in many cities in South America, Africa, and Asia there are thousands of people who leave their homes in the countryside every year to look for work.

Often there are no jobs for them in the city and they finish up with no money at all. Where can they live if they have no money? These people build houses from things that others have thrown away, such as pieces of wood, tin, and cardboard. They live without all the things many of us take for granted, like electricity, drinking water, and indoor toilets.

Most homes are divided into spaces or rooms that are supposed to be used for different activities—the bedroom for sleeping, the bathroom for bathing, the kitchen for cooking, the dining room for eating, and the living room for things like talking to friends and watching TV. Because it is usually the biggest room in the home, the living room is where special events like birthday parties are held.

Originally people in cold climates divided their homes into rooms that could be shut off from each other to save heat. A fire could be lit in one room, which would stay warm while the rest of the house

was allowed to get cold. Another reason for dividing houses into rooms is to allow people to do different things at the same time without disturbing each other. If someone is playing the piano in the living room, you can go to your bedroom to read. A closed door says "please leave me alone," or "knock before entering."

There is probably something different or special about each room in your home. Perhaps one room has a fireplace or a high ceiling. Maybe one looks out at the schoolyard across the street, and from another one you can see a tall building far away. Some homes have basements and attics and an upstairs and a downstairs. Basements are dark and cool and attics are dusty and hot. Do you have a favourite place at home? In winter? In summer?

Home is more than just bricks and wood and cement. Home is important to us because it is probably the one place in the world where we can really be ourselves.

THE GENERAL

by Frank Etherington

T he Bridgeport General had torn all the buttons off his long coat. He didn't like buttons and zippers, he used large safety pins to close his coat.

When Jainin first met the General, she was six years old and much too shy to speak to him. At home, when she talked to her older brother, Jacob, and her parents, she called him Mr. General.

He got his nickname because of the army-style coat and metal helmet he wore. The helmet was shaped like a flying saucer and had once belonged to a Canadian soldier.

Under his coat, the General wore a leather vest. He didn't have any shirts and, no matter how hot or cold it got, summer or winter, he always had on the same clothes. The only change he ever made was when he left his metal helmet at home and wore a peaked cap that had flaps to keep his ears warm.

He had a battered, home-made stop sign and, for many years, had helped kids cross Lancaster Street on their way to Bridgeport School. Jainin's dad said the General never got paid for his work but did it because he liked kids and wanted something to do with his time.

Jainin was scared of the General when her family first moved to Bridgeport. She thought he looked very strange. Although she never said anything about his clothes, other kids often did.

Some of them shouted cruel names at him and said he looked like a rag bag. The kids would run away when he shook his stop sign at them. If ever anyone asked about his clothes and stayed around long enough to listen, his answer was always the same:

"Look, I wear them because I want to wear them," he said. "Those who think my clothes are stupid wear what they want to wear. Everyone to his own liking. These clothes keep me cool in the summer and warm in the winter."

The General also wore a pair of mitts and large rubber boots.

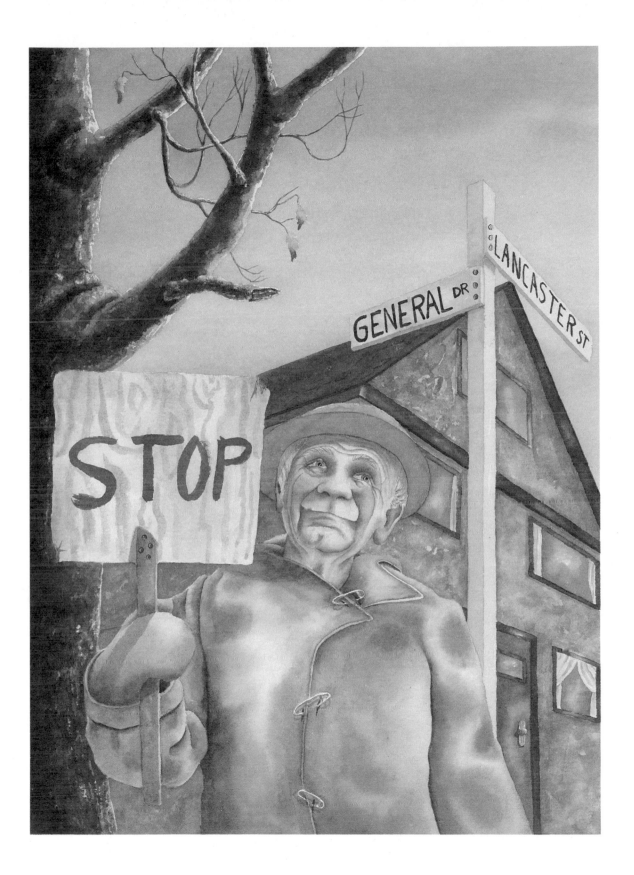

It was a misty, wet September day when Jainin left home with Jacob to start her first day at school. They walked together down Bridge Street to the crossing. There was a gas station, a butcher's store, a place called the Grand Hotel and a bank with a broken clock at the intersection.

Jainin was sticking her tongue out trying to catch rain dripping off her rain hat when the General met them at the intersection. He noticed Jainin's rubber boots.

"Look at that," he said as the cars and trucks splashed by and rain dribbled down his soldier's helmet. "You got baby General boots."

Under her rain hat, Jainin looked down where her boots poked out the bottom of her long raincoat. She was too shy to answer the General who was measuring one of his boots beside her feet.

"How come your boots are so big?" he asked. "They look too big for your body. You got big feet like me?"

Jainin leaned close to Jacob and didn't say a word.

"She's shy," said Jacob who was eight and a half years old. "Those used to be my boots and she's growing into them. It's her first day at a new school and she's scared. I ain't scared."

"Whatsername?" said the General bending down to peek under Jainin's hat.

"Her name's Jainin. It's spelled J-A-I-N-I-N," said Jacob. "She's six and she'll be seven tomorrow 'cos it's her birthday."

"Well Jainin," said the General, careful to say the name correctly, "because you got big feet and General boots and, because it's your birthday tomorrow, I got something special for you."

Jainin looked up as he pushed a glove inside one of his coat pockets.

"Here," he said, "that's for a kid on her first day at a new school."

Jainin took the gift but, before she had time to look, the General walked into the middle of the road. With both hands held in the air he stopped two cars and a dump truck. Jainin, Jacob and some other kids crossed the road and walked up the hill towards their school.

"See you guys at lunchtime," shouted the General. "Don't go rusty in the rain."

When she got to the school playground, Jainin looked down to see what the General had given her.

"Let me see," said Jacob. "It's just a bunch of old beer-bottle caps tied up with wire."

"It's a very pretty bracelet," said Jainin slipping the blue and red bottle caps over her hand.

At school her teacher, Mrs. Schmidt, made name tags for Jainin and two other new kids. She was trying to spell Jainin's name right when she noticed the bracelet.

"Mr. General at the crossing gave it to me," Jainin said.

"The Bridgeport General always has something special for someone on their first day at school," said Mrs. Schmidt. "He's been doing it for as long as I can remember, and I've been here for ten years. It's a lovely bracelet," she said handing Jainin a name tag spelled JANINE.

It didn't seem to trouble the General much when Jainin was too shy to speak. He had sometimes seen her watching when he walked up the railway tracks near her home collecting bottles and he knew that they were friends.

It was different for Jainin to meet older people like the General. She had grandparents but, because they lived a long way away, she saw them only once a year.

Before they moved to Bridgeport, Jainin's family had lived in a new subdivision on the outskirts of the nearby city of Kitchener. All of the people that lived in the subdivision were much younger than the General.

It was only when her family moved to the little village by the Grand River that Jainin started to meet older people. She enjoyed being with them because they made her laugh and often did things that kids like to do.

Jainin also liked them because they were never too busy to listen and seemed to share a problem that most kids had with their parents. The problem was that, every time kids or old people were around, parents became impatient and didn't want to pay attention.

"They're always busy, busy trying to make lots of money and rushing around all over the place," the General told Jainin one day at the crossing. "They never got time to stop and talk."

He told Jainin he had never been on vacation but liked to get letters in the mail. His favourite postcards had pictures of people smiling on sunny beaches and kids splashing in the ocean.

When the cards arrived, they were addressed to The General, Bridgeport, Ontario. Because the village mailman knew the General so well, his mail always arrived safely at his home.

Jainin also helped the General search for bottles around the village. Some days they would walk along the river bank picking up garbage and collecting bottles.

Once, when Jainin and the General were walking near the railway tracks, they found a wallet full of money. They took it to the village police chief who returned the wallet and money to a man who worked on the railway.

A few days later the General went to Jainin's house while she was at school. He told her mom that the man who owned the wallet had sent a $10 reward.

"Jainin helped find it so I brought her $5," he said.

When Jainin got home she said she would spend some of the money on a birthday present for the General.

"I don't think he gets many presents. The problem is, I don't know when his birthday is," she said.

"Ask him," said her dad. So she did.

"When's yours?" asked the General.

"September the fifth," answered Jainin.

"Can't remember when I was born," he said, "I just know it was a long, long time ago."

Jainin told him that if he couldn't remember he could share her birthday.

When September 5 arrived he gave her a silver pocketwatch that didn't work, wrapped in a piece of soft velvet. Jainin went to the drug store and bought him a package of large safety pins after she noticed that the ones on his coat were getting rusty.

Because the General was so pleased with his birthday gift, Jainin told her family she was going to get him a special Christmas present. During the next few months she spent a lot of time thinking about what she could give to the General.

One afternoon, when Bridgeport School was closed on a teacher-training day, Jainin's mom took her Christmas shopping in the city. When the bus passed a school crossing guard in Kitchener, Jainin suddenly had an idea.

"That's what I could get him. He doesn't have a very good stop sign. I could make him one."

"You could do it in the garage this weekend," her mom said. "I'm sure your dad has stuff you could use to make a sign."

Jainin's dad thought the stop sign was a great idea for a present. Together they searched through the garage that night and found some red paint, a handle from an old snow shovel and a metal circle her dad had brought home from the hardware store where he worked.

On Friday evening, Jainin spread out some newspapers in the garage and found herself a paint brush. Before she went to bed, she painted the metal circle.

Later, while her dad helped to scrub paint off her fingers, Jainin explained how she would borrow her mother's stencils to write letters on the sign. Jacob glanced up from a comic book he was reading and said she could use a can of white paint he had bought to decorate his bike.

The next day, when the red paint was dry, Jainin arranged the stencils on the metal circle and wrote STOP with the white paint. She used a saw to cut a slot in the top of the snow shovel handle and a nail to attach the handle to the red circle.

After lunch she wrapped up the sign and made a Christmas card to tell the General that the sign was a present from her family.

The General was chipping ice from the sidewalk outside Mrs. Crump's house when Jacob and Jainin took him the gift on Christmas Eve morning.

"This is for you, for Christmas," Jainin said.

The General stopped his work and looked at the huge parcel.

"You're kidding," he said, "What's in there? A new snow shovel?"

"You're not supposed to see it until Christmas but, because we won't see you, we want you to open it now," said Jainin.

"Well, let's get in here out of the wind," he said, leading Jainin and Jacob into the shelter of Mrs. Crump's porch. He put down his shovel and looked at the package.

The General had difficulty undoing the string around the parcel because he didn't take off his leather mitts. Jainin and Jacob helped him untie the knots.

"I'll be. . . . " said the General, when he saw the sign, "Ain't you kids nice, ain't you nice."

He looked like he wanted to hug them but didn't know how. Instead, he did a very strange thing.

"You kids going home now?" he asked.

"Yes," said Jainin, "we have other presents to wrap."

"That means you have to go across the street, right? So that'll give me a chance to try my new sign," he said.

"But there's no school," said Jainin.

"And no cars coming," added Jacob.

"Don't matter," said the General. "We'll just wait for some cars."

He took Jainin and Jacob down to the intersection and waited in the snow until a bus came down the street.

The General walked out waving his new sign while the bus driver stopped, honked his horn and opened his passenger doors. People on the bus clapped and cheered when they saw the new stop sign.

"Finally got yourself a decent sign?" laughed the bus driver.

"Yep, just got it from these kids for Christmas," said the General. Then he marched Jainin and Jacob across to the opposite side of the street.

All that day, he used the new sign to stop traffic every time Christmas shoppers wanted to cross the street. Jainin's dad said the General was still stopping cars when he drove home from work.

From that day on, the General carried the sign that Jainin made for him.

THE UNBELIEVABLE

Somewhere behind
the flower shop or whatever
fronted King Street there
                  two trees
or skeletons of trees, still growing,
still fighting to stay alive
in a place where no life was meant to be

And none of us knew this
until today:
              when with buildings levelled,
we looked across this brick-and-rubble wasteland
and saw the unbelievable—
                    scrawny limbs, poor arms,
straining upward to touch the sun.

NOBODY'S TOLD THE BIRDS

Nobody's told the birds
that this house has been sold to the wreckers,
nobody's told the birds
that the creepers on the north wall that hide
their nests from the squirrels will die
along with the wall they cling to,
as the crowbars stab brick by brick,
as the bulldozer panzers level off
stubborn stone to a joyless rubble.

Nobody's told the birds,
so they sing on day after day,
and no doubt will be singing the hour
that the crowbars pierce their last brick,
that the bulldozer cuts its hacking cough.
That song will follow right along
to the next house, the next and the next,
a loud song of gladness and light.

Nobody's told the birds,
so that song will go on forever.

Poems by Raymond Souster

from

PEEWEE

by Suzanne Martel

O nly a few of the big overhead lights pierced the gloom of the huge, empty arena. Up in the stands, Mr. Dugré was noisily repairing benches. Loud hammering echoed back and forth, drowning out the rhythmic sound of skates slicing across the ice.

From time to time, the janitor looked up and shook his head as he watched the tiny figure going round and round the ice with stubborn determination.

For two weeks now, Yves had been practising at the rink. Each day he would quietly sneak in through the side door which the gruff old man left open for him. Stashing his bicycle under the stairs, he would look around furtively. Then he would pull his skates, a heavy sweater and a book out of the brown paper bag he had brought with him.

The book, entitled *The Secrets of Hockey*, was his constant guide and companion these days. Even though he already knew it by heart, Yves kept it on the edge of the boards and consulted it frequently, barely able to make out the words in the dim light.

Balance: Skate into the turns, leaning towards the centre. Start by skating in a wide circle. Remember to bend your knees and arch your back, keeping your head up at all times.

Quietly repeating this advice to himself, Yves skated round the rink, trying to think everything all at once: arms, legs, head, ankles. He felt like an off-balance centipede. Gee, it was complicated! Yet when he watched the Canadiens on television, everything looked so easy! How would he ever be able to stickhandle the puck if he didn't even know what to do with his arms in the turns?

Just when he thought he had his feet under control, the top of his skate would catch on the ice and whoops! down he'd go with a thud. But he'd immediately get up and start again, gritting his teeth, determined to succeed no matter what.

Frowning as usual, Mr. Dugré observed him from the top of the stands. "No doubt about it, the little squirt is really coming along," he said to himself. "The way he keeps at it, he's going to make it for sure." Then, as if to punish himself for having kind thoughts, the old man hammered just a little harder and pounded in the last nail. "That's all for today. I'm closing up now."

"Already? I was just beginning to get the hang of turning right." Yves' clear voice echoed through the empty arena. Not about to give in, the janitor gathered up his tools and marched down the stairs. "I'm closing up, I said. Now come on—get out of here!"

"See you tomorrow, Mr. Dugré. And thanks again. I'll dedicate my first goal to you."

"Get it first! Then we'll see," he grumbled as he turned the key in the lock.

They headed off in opposite directions, the boy tired out but happy, and the crusty old man muttering something about pesky kids who made his work as a janitor ten times harder.

HOCKEY MASKS

painted by Michael Cutler

Wayne Stephenson, Philadelphia Flyers

Grant Fuhr, Edmonton Oilers

Ken Dryden, Montreal Canadiens

Mario Lessard, Los Angeles Kings

All of the hockey masks shown here were designed by Greg Harrison with the exception of Ken Dryden's mask which was designed by Carl Lamb and Mr. Dryden. They are reproduced from paintings by Michael Cutler taken from his book GREAT HOCKEY MASKS © 1983 published by Tundra Books.

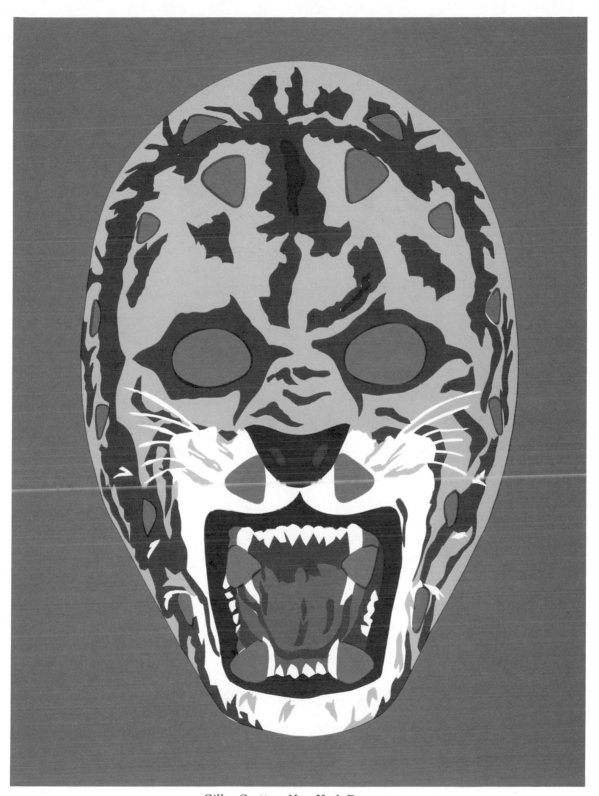

Gilles Gratton, New York Rangers

Murray Bannerman, Chicago Black Hawks

Gilles Meloche, Cleveland Barons

Ed Staniowski, St. Louis Blues

Curt Ridley, Vancouver Canucks

Al Smith, Buffalo Sabres

GRETZKY

by Meguido Zola

Saturday night. It's *Hockey Night in Canada* on TV. In the living room of Wayne Gretzky's grandparents, everyone is watching two NHL teams battling out the last minutes of a cliff-hanger.

Suddenly, there he is: Wayne Gretzky! He's charging the goal-mouth. He shoots! He scores!

Wayne has just scored the first goal of his life. He is not even two years old. The goaltender he has beaten is his grandmother—sitting in the big armchair in front of the TV.

As he does every Saturday night, Wayne is whizzing around the floor of the living room. He has one eye on his toy hockey stick and ball. His other eye is on the TV players he is imitating.

Yes, "The Kid's" hockey career is off to an early start.

And a *good* start, too. The best start possible—the support and encouragement of his parents.

"Wayne's hockey didn't just happen by itself," explains his mother. "But then we didn't push him into it, either. What we did was . . . create the environment."

"And a big part of that environment was sport," Wayne's father adds. "I believe in sport because it teaches you an important lesson about life: that if you want something, you have to go for it. Sport teaches you to work hard, to stand on your own two feet, to discipline yourself."

"Yes, I learned a lot in those early years," Wayne agrees. "To give the game everything. To do only my very best. *Every* time."

Wayne Douglas Gretzky was born on January 26, 1961, in Brantford, Ontario.

His parents, Walter and Phyllis Gretzky, put skates on their son just after his second birthday.

After that, they turned the yard behind the house into a rink. In the early winter, after the ground froze, they cut the grass short. Then, using the lawn sprinkler, they flooded the ground with layer

after layer of ice. Wayne's father added nets and a huge spotlight. He put up pylons as obstacles for Wayne to skate patterns around. And over the years he put Wayne through all kinds of drills and shooting exercises. Many of these training ideas became popular in Canada only some years later—after the 1972 series between Canada and the Soviet Union.

For Wayne—and the friends he always invited over—that bumpy back-yard rink became the centre of activity, the scene of all the action.

"It was my favourite place," Wayne says. "Day or night. In good weather or bad. Alone or with my buddies. I practised and practised. Hours and hours on end."

"And if he wasn't there," remembers his father, "he'd be firing a ball against the wall. Always with a stick and puck, or stick and ball, that was Wayne."

At the age of only five, Wayne joined his first league. His team was the Nadrofsky Steelers of his home town.

As he was to do for years to come, Wayne played with and against players much older and bigger than he was. That is how he got nicknamed "The Kid." But, kid or no kid, the "Great Gretzky" was already dazzling everyone.

In that first season of 1967–68, Wayne scored one goal. He scored 27 goals the following season, 104 the next, and 196 the year after that. In 1971–72, his last season in Novice, Wayne scored an incredible 378 goals in 85 games.

During the next two seasons, Wayne played Major Peewee. He scored 104 goals his first year and 176 goals his second. Over those years, Wayne's team seldom lost a game or a tournament. Wayne himself broke record after record.

A game against Waterford on April 10, 1974, is just one example of such a special occasion. "Gretzky got the puck inside the Waterford blue line and let go with a slapshot," the *Brantford Expositor* reported. "The Waterford goalie got a piece of the puck, but not enough to keep it from going into the net. Players rushed onto the ice, and the game was held up for several minutes. Gretzky had

scored his 1000th career goal."

Being a hockey star at such a young age created problems for Wayne.

He was always on show, often in the limelight. Before he was ten years old, he had to put up with being followed around by the press. He had to learn to give interviews for TV and radio. He had to get used to signing autographs for fans and to having his stick or gloves stolen as souvenirs.

"All this attention," Wayne remembers, "meant that I was a marked man. People—mostly parents, sometimes a coach—picked on me and got on my back."

If Wayne's team was losing, people might ask why he wasn't doing this or wasn't doing that. If his team was winning, they figured he should be on the bench to give others more ice time.

Some parents would get jealous. They booed when Wayne made a good play and cheered when he was knocked down.

On the rink players might hassle Wayne by slashing or high-sticking. One coach even offered $25 to anyone who could knock

Wayne out of the game. (Nobody collected.)

Off the ice, there could be violence too—name-calling, bullying and, once, a group of older boys plotting to beat Wayne up after an out-of-town game. The police had to be called in to protect Wayne and his team.

Throughout all this, Wayne was helped by the support and encouragement of his parents. His teammates, too, always stuck up for him. They admired the star who brought out the best in them. They loved the friend who was so unselfish, patient and cheerful.

When Wayne was fourteen, the Gretzkys came to a tough decision. They agreed to let Wayne leave home to play hockey in Toronto.

In his home town, Wayne was getting too much attention—the good kind and the bad kind. The pressure was taking the fun out of hockey. And it was making it hard for Wayne to live a normal life like any other boy his age.

In Toronto, Wayne went to live with family friends. He was going to join a Bantam team, but the plan didn't work out. Wayne wasn't allowed to play Bantam in Toronto because of certain rules of the Ontario Minor Hockey Association. So he went up to Junior B, which did not come under the same rules.

It was late in the season when Wayne joined the Toronto Young Nationals, and in Junior he had to play against men up to twenty years old. All the same, Wayne won the league's Rookie-of-the-Year award!

During his two seasons in Junior B hockey, Wayne kept in close touch with his parents. He called home every night, and the family would drive to as many of his games as they could.

But those years and the next few were not easy for the young boy. Away from home so much of the time, Wayne had to get used to new places and to living with different families. He had to change schools several times, and he also had to do some of his school work by correspondence.

In this way, Wayne grew up fast. He learned to mix with different people and to make friends quickly. He also learned to be self-reliant and independent.

At the age of sixteen Wayne was drafted third in the country to play Junior A for the Sault Ste. Marie Greyhounds.

Wayne's play thrilled the fans. They flocked in record numbers to watch what became known as "The Wayne Gretzky Show." He scored 70 goals and 112 assists in 64 games and was voted the league's Rookie of the Year and its most sportsmanlike player.

Wayne had been equally outstanding in that year's World Junior Tournament in Montreal. Although he was the youngest player in the tournament, he was its top scorer with eight goals and nine assists.

Two other important things happened that season.

First, Gus Badali had become Wayne's agent. Gus has watched over Wayne's career with skill and tact and has become a close personal and family friend.

Second, Wayne acquired his famous Number 99. He had wanted 9—for his hero Gordie Howe—but another player already had it. Somehow other numbers just didn't feel right. Finally, at coach Muzz MacPherson's suggestion, Wayne tried and settled on 99. He has worn 99 ever since.

Wayne turned professional in 1978 at the age of only seventeen.

He played first for the Indianapolis Racers of the World Hockey Association. Then, after only a few games, financial problems forced the Racers' owner to sell Wayne's contract to Peter Pocklington, the owner of the Edmonton Oilers.

In his first professional year, Wayne never missed a game. He finished the season with a record 110 points, and he was named the WHA's Rookie of the Year.

That year, Wayne also had the thrill of skating on the same line as Gordie Howe when the WHA All-Stars played the Moscow Dynamo in a three-game series.

"It scares me how good he could become!" raved Gordie Howe.

The next year, the WHA merged with the National Hockey League. In his first year in the NHL, Wayne surprised everyone with another phenomenal performance. He tied with Marcel Dionne for the league scoring leadership with 137 points. The trophy went

to Dionne because he had scored more goals, but Wayne won the Hart Trophy as the league's Most Valuable Player. He also won the Lady Byng Trophy for being the most sportsmanlike player.

Wayne won the Hart Trophy again the following year, as well as the Art Ross Trophy for the most points of the season. And he continued to break NHL records, including those for assists in one season and points in one season.

His play carried the Edmonton Oilers past the Montreal Canadiens in the biggest upset of the Stanley Cup playoffs. It also carried the Oilers on to give the New York Islanders their only tough competition on their way to a second straight Stanley Cup.

What is the secret of Wayne Gretzky's success? What makes him "The Great Gretzky," as he is usually called? It's not one thing, but a combination of several.

Wayne has a store of God-given abilities that have been developed by endless hard work and the coaching of his father. These natural gifts include intelligence, fast reflexes and an unusual capacity to renew his energy instantly.

Wayne's stickhandling is deft and uncanny. He has bomb-sight passing skills (along with a knack for setting up goals for his teammates). His shot is not strong, but it is deadly accurate.

Perhaps his most striking ability is his anticipation. He always seems to know where every player is, and where he is going; where the puck is, and what it will do.

But hockey is not all smooth going for Wayne Gretzky.

The 1981 Canada Cup tournament is an example. Wayne was the top scorer in the series; he was twice Team Canada's Most Valuable Player; and he was everybody's favourite. But in the last game of the finals, Canada lost 8–1 to the Soviet Union. It was a terrible disappointment to everyone, and especially to Wayne.

"It's the biggest downfall I've ever had. I felt I let my country down. All I wanted to do was go far away. I hid for days. Nobody knew where I was." But Wayne did not let defeat trouble him for long.

"It showed that I'm still young. That I'm going to make mistakes. That I've got a lot to learn."

And, as always, he just set about polishing up his game.

Like his plays on the ice, Wayne's contracts attract a lot of attention. They earn him fabulous amounts of money—not to mention such nicknames as "Brinks" and "The Franchise."

Wayne became a millionaire on his eighteenth birthday. He signed a multi-million dollar, 21-year contract, the longest ever in pro hockey.

Over the next three years, Wayne became the highest paid player in the game's history. Then in 1982, just before his twenty-first birthday, he signed a new 21-year contract. This one would pay him over a million dollars a year and give him such extras as his own shopping centre.

"You can't put a price on greatness," explains Oilers owner Peter Pocklington.

But whatever his earnings, Wayne follows Gordie Howe's advice to him: "No matter how much you make, get out there and earn it."

That's exactly what Wayne does, as he showed when he broke yet another record. Since the 1970–71 season, Phil Esposito had held the record for the most goals in a single season—76. On Wednesday, February 24, 1982, in a game against the Buffalo Sabres, Wayne scored his 77th goal of the season. Within minutes he had added a 78th and a 79th!

A month later, on March 25, Wayne again made hockey history by getting his 200th point of the season. By the time the regular season was over, he had an incredible 212 points.

Much of Wayne's earnings, including the money he makes from advertising various products, goes into savings. Wayne himself draws only a small amount in spending money. He offered to buy a new house for his parents, but they refused. They preferred to continue living in the home where the Gretzky family grew up.

Riches, like fame, have not spoiled Wayne. Quite the opposite. For all the demands that are made on him, he gives generously of his time to support such organizations as the Canadian Association for the Mentally Retarded, the Heart Fund, the United Appeal, the Red Cross, and others.

Whatever the occasion—signing hockey cards for kids, doing an interview, appearing for charitable causes—Wayne gives freely, he gives fully. He gives *himself*.

"It's difficult to say no," he says.

"Wayne'll do anything," says a reporter. "He thinks he *should*. He thinks he *has* to."

"I'm just a country Canadian," Wayne says about himself. Indeed, he is natural and down to earth, a simple and warm person with an attractive personality.

He is thoughtful and patient. He is modest about himself—almost shy—and he has a knack for making others feel at ease.

"One thing always being in the public eye has done is teach me self-discipline."

Wayne remembers the advice his father gave him when he was just a boy.

"You're a special person, Wayne. All your life people are going to watch you, and follow you, and fuss over you. You'll always be on display and you've got to behave right."

Like his hero, Gordie Howe, this is exactly what Wayne sets out to be, both on the ice and off it: an example to others, especially young people.

For those who want to play sports, Wayne has some important tips.

"Make sure, whatever happens, that you enjoy it—otherwise what's the sense in playing? Enjoy it and give it your best shot, your all. Then, don't try to be someone or something you're not: instead, just do what *you* do best."

And Wayne has some things to say to parents.

"Give your kids every opportunity possible. *Always* take an interest and be supportive. (If I had a son playing hockey, for instance, I'd go to every game of his, just like my dad did.) Don't knock your kids. Don't pressure them. Recognize that everyone has different sorts of talents and accept it. Respect your kids and let them have fun."

Today, Wayne Gretzky is one of hockey's most intelligent and skillful offensive players, as well as its most effective scorer. At the end of the regular season in 1986, after only seven years as a professional player, Wayne's career point total stood at 1337! He is also surely the most exciting and fun to watch. And he is the most popular player in the game.

But, more than all that, we know that Wayne Gretzky is still young. We know that he is still maturing, still striving to perfect his game. As good as he is now, the best is yet to come for Wayne.

SKIPPING RHYMES

Wire, briar, limberlock,
Three geese in a flock.
One flew east, and one flew west,
And one flew over the cuckoo's nest.
How many eggs were in the nest?
1, 2, 3, etc.

My mother owns a butcher shop,
My father cuts the meat,
And I am just their little kid,
Who runs across the street.
How many times do I cross?
1, 2, 3, etc.

Doctor, doctor, tell no lie,
How many years before I die?
1, 2, 3, etc.

One, two, three, four, five,
I caught a mackerel-fish alive.
Six, seven, eight, nine, ten,
I threw the fish back in again.
How many times did I do that?
1, 2, 3, etc.

Doctor, doctor, tell me quick,
How many days will I be sick?
1, 2, 3, etc.

Billy gave me apples,
Billy gave me pears.
Billy gave me fifty cents,
And kissed me on the stairs.
I gave him back his apples,
I gave him back his pears.
I gave him back his fifty cents,
And kicked him down the stairs.
How many stairs did he roll down?
1, 2, 3, etc.

Postman, postman, do your duty.
Mail this letter to my cutie.
Postman, postman, don't delay,
Send it to him (her) right away.
How many days will the letter take?
1, 2, 3, etc.

Last night, the night before,
A lemon and a pickle
Came knocking at my door.
I opened the door, to let them in,
And they hit me on the head
With a rolling pin.
How many times
Did they hit me on the head?
1, 2, 3, etc.

THE BACK OF THE CAVE

Why do many people find dinosaurs so interesting? After all, they have been extinct for millions of years. It seems that we are still interested in what went on in the past. Stories about cave men, explorers, and pioneers continue to interest us. Someone once said that we can hope for tomorrow only if we can understand yesterday. Imagine, then, the excitement of the children who find a creature from the past in their own community.

"Quick, Stig, they're coming!" exclaimed Barney. "Get back into our hiding place!" And he pulled Stig back into the mouth of the earth. As he did so a large fox-hound came out onto the track and lolloped towards them on the scent of the fox. It came straight for where they were hiding, looked up and saw Stig, and bared its teeth and growled.

Stig bared his teeth and growled.

The hound looked surprised. It wasn't sure whether Stig was animal or human, but he was certainly lying between it and a good strong scent.

The hound took a step forward, making horrible noises in his throat.

Stig took a step forward on his hands and knees, making horrible noises in his throat.

Barney sat at the back of the little cave, holding his middle. The hound looked very big and fierce and he was afraid it might hurt Stig. But then Stig was looking very fierce too, and he might hurt the hound.

Stig was the first to move. With a lightning spring he darted forward and bit the hound hard on the ear. It was too much for the poor animal. It was not afraid of sharp-toothed foxes or other animals that fought back, but Stig smelt like a man and it had never heard of a man biting a dog. It turned and made off yelping, with its tail between its legs.

Barney looked at Stig. "I think we better go home," he said. "We're supposed to be fox hunting and what have you done? Killed a pheasant, helped a fox, and bitten a hound! What are you going to do next, I'd like to know?"

(from *Stig of the Dump*, by Clive King)

What do you think Stig, this character from the past, will do next? Can a person from another time exist in today's world?

This section contains several selections about the past, and you will be reading stories about your grandparents' early days as well as stories from the back of the cave.

PATRICK'S DINOSAURS

by Carol Carrick

Patrick and his brother, Hank, went to the zoo on Saturday. They stood outside a tall fence and watched the elephants.

"I'll bet that elephant is the biggest animal in the whole world," said Patrick.

"You think he's big," Hank said. "A brontosaurus was heavier than TEN elephants."

"Gosh!" said Patrick. If Hank said so, it must be true. Hank knew all about dinosaurs. He knew more about everything because he was older and went to school already.

Patrick squeezed his eyes half shut. What would a dinosaur that weighed as much as ten elephants look like? The brontosaurus he imagined turned and looked right at him.

"Did a brontosaurus eat people?" he asked nervously.

"Just plants," answered Hank.

Patrick's dinosaur started eating leaves from one of the trees.

They went to see the crocodiles next. Crocs were Patrick's favourite because he liked to scare himself.

"Those are shrimpy," said Hank. "In the days of dinosaurs, crocodiles grew three times that big."

"Wow!" said Patrick.

"Just their JAWS were twice as big as you are," added Hank.

Patrick imagined an enormous crocodile. It was three times bigger than the other crocs. It was so big that it wanted the whole pool for itself.

The other crocodiles were too slow getting out. So the enormous crocodile opened its jaws that were twice as big as Patrick and gobbled them all up.

Patrick backed away. "We didn't see the monkeys yet."

After they had seen the monkeys and the seals, Patrick and Hank went for a row on the zoo lake.

Patrick looked down into the deep green water. What was that dark shape next to their boat? "Did dinosaurs know how to swim?" he asked.

"Some did," answered Hank. "Diplodocus, the longest dinosaur, could stay under water like a submarine because its nose was on top of its head."

Patrick was afraid to move. Out of the corner of his eyes he saw the big thing swimming along next to them. It might rise and dump them over!

"WHAT'S THAT!" he cried. "We're going to bump into it!"

"No, dopey. That's just the shadow from our boat," Hank explained.

Patrick wasn't so sure. "Let's go home now," he said. "Rowing makes me tired."

When they got on the bus, Patrick felt better, even though Hank was still showing off how much he knew about dinosaurs.

"A stegosaurus was bigger than one of those cars," Hank said. "But its brain was only the size of a walnut."

Patrick looked out of the window. In his mind the lane of cars was a line of walnut-brained stegosauruses. The plates on their backs swayed like sails as they plodded along.

Hank reached up and rang the bell for the driver to stop. "A triceratops was tougher than a stegosaurus," he said. "It could even take on a tyrannosaurus."

The bus stopped at their corner. On the other side of the street Patrick thought he saw a triceratops waiting for the traffic light.

When Patrick and his brother climbed down from the bus, the hot dusty street became a prehistoric forest. Tropical birds screamed their warning. Too late. A dreadful tyrannosaurus crashed into the clearing.

Patrick held his breath as the triceratops lowered its huge head. Its horns pointed ahead like three enormous spears. When the traffic light changed, the triceratops charged.

"RUN!" Patrick yelled. He headed for their apartment building.

"What's the hurry?" called Hank.

Patrick didn't feel safe until the front door of the hall slammed shut. He wanted to look out his window, but first he had to ask Hank something.

"How big was a tyrannosaurus?"

"Big," said Hank.

"Up to the second floor, maybe?" asked Patrick.

"At least," Hank agreed.

"That's what I was afraid of," said Patrick.

He peeked into his bedroom. Sure enough, the ugly head of the tyrannosaurus almost filled his window.

The dinosaur opened its mouth to show teeth like daggers. Patrick didn't think this dinosaur ate leaves.

"Are you SURE there are no more dinosaurs around?" he asked Hank.

"Positive. The dinosaurs have been gone for sixty million years."

Patrick gave a sigh of relief. And the dinosaur disappeared.

DINOSAURS

by Keith Moseley

T he dinosaurs ruled the earth for many millions of years. They first appeared about 225 million years ago. The last of the dinosaurs died about 65 million years ago—long before the appearance of humans.

The name "dinosaur" means "terrible lizard," but many dinosaurs were not terrible and none were lizards. Though there were some small dinosaurs—one no bigger than a chicken—most of them were large and some were enormous, as tall as a five-storey building. Yet most of the dinosaurs were peaceful plant eaters. Only a few kinds were meat eaters.

Most of what we know about the dinosaurs is based on our studies of bones and teeth, now turned to fossils. The first dinosaur fossils were found as early as 1677 in England. Since then fossilized bones, teeth, footprints, or skin prints have been found in many parts of the world.

The world of dinosaurs was very different from the one we know today. There were few large animals or plants that we could recognize. The continents and the seas were not the same as those we know. The dinosaurs lived and died in a world no longer with us.

Coelophysis is one of the earliest dinosaurs that lived in North America. Its skeleton reveals that *Coelophysis* walked on strong hind legs, had a long, birdlike neck, a small head, and a long tail. Its bones were hollow. Its sharp teeth tell us that it was a meat eater. Similar birdlike dinosaurs have been found in Germany, Scotland and Africa.

Coelophysis was not a very big dinosaur. About a metre tall at the hips, *Coelophysis* weighed not much more than 45 kg and looked something like a large bird without feathers. Scientists believe its skin was scaly, like a lizard's.

Coelophysis was a swift runner. With its great speed and sharp teeth, it probably caught and ate small lizards, early mammals (furry,

shrewlike egg layers), as well as insects such as cockroaches and dragonflies. Also, it may have hunted in packs, as wolves do today. A group of these small dinosaurs could even have attacked and eaten larger, plant-eating dinosaurs.

Coelophysis probably laid small eggs and cared for its young after the eggs hatched, much the way birds do. In fact, some scientists think that *Coelophysis* was warm-blooded and that these small, hollow-boned dinosaurs may have been the ancient ancestors of birds.

Perhaps the most familiar dinosaurs are those with long necks and tails, small heads, and thick, treelike legs. These dinosaurs usually walked on all four feet and ate the leaves of tall plants. They belong to a group of dinosaurs called SAUROPODS, which means "lizard foot."

Brachiosaurus was the largest of the SAUROPODS, possibly the largest animal that ever lived on land. This enormous creature was taller than a four-storey building and weighed as much as twelve large elephants. It lived in the forests of western North America and East Africa more than 100 million years ago.

Like all SAUROPODS, *Brachiosaurus* had thick, stumpy legs and big feet. It was called *Brachiosaurus*, which means "arm lizard," because—unlike most other SAUROPODS—its front legs were much longer than its hind legs.

Brachiosaurus fed from the leaves at the tops of trees, the way giraffes do today. With its seven-metre-long neck, *Brachiosaurus* could reach the tops of twelve-metre trees. Though its head was small and its jaws not very strong, *Brachiosaurus* had a large stomach to hold all the food it needed to provide energy for its huge body.

Brachiosaurus was a slow-moving animal that depended upon its size for survival. It must have been successful, because it lived on the earth for many millions of years. Some scientists believe that a few individuals may have lived to be 200 years old.

More than 100 million years ago, much of the world was under water and the continents we know today were just beginning to take shape. In those times, the giant reptiles of the seas were the *Plesiosaurs*. Some *Plesiosaurs* were twelve to fifteen metres long. Their

skeletons show that the *Plesiosaurs* had squat bodies and stubby tails, but long necks. They swam with powerful strokes of their broad, paddle-shaped legs.

Scientists studying their skeletons believe that the *Plesiosaurs* could swim just as well backward as forward. They could probably turn their bodies around instantly by stroking on one side and "backing water" on the other. *Plesiosaurs* were mainly fish eaters.

Ichthyosaurs were similar animals that swam in those ancient seas. The *Ichthyosaurs* were reptiles but their bodies resembled the dolphins of today. Like dolphins, the *Ichthyosaurs* could swim as well as fish and gave birth to live young in the water.

The largest flesh eater of all time was the *Tyrannosaurus rex*. Its name means "king of the tyrant lizards." This enormous hunter

measured more than twelve metres from nose to tail and had a mass of five or six tonnes. It stood six metres high on its hind legs—as tall as a two-story house. *Tyrannosaurus* fossils have been found in the northwest regions of North America.

Tyrannosaurus had a huge head, more than 120 cm long from front to back. Its teeth were 15 cm long and jagged on each side—ideal for cutting up meat.

Like many other dinosaur hunters, *Tyrannosaurus* stood on its hind legs. It probably could not run as fast as *Allosaurus* or some of the smaller hunters. But its leg strength was important in capturing and holding its prey. Its great feet had four toes—three that pointed forward and one reversed.

Tyrannosaurus had small arms with two tiny fingers. They would have been useless for catching anything. Some scientists believe that the arms were useful in helping the huge animal rise from a lying position on the ground.

Many dinosaurs were well adapted to defend themselves against attack.

Stegosaurus was a large, plated dinosaur. It was a plant eater whose defence was its armour. Even though *Stegosaurus* was about the size of an elephant, it had a very small head, a little more than 30 cm long. Two rows of bony plates ran along its back and down part of its tail, which was also barbed with bony spikes. Despite its armour, *Stegosaurus* was no match for the flesh eaters that preyed upon it.

Triceratops was a plant eater with an enormous armoured head. Its skull measured more than two metres from its nose to its neck shield. The horns above its eyes were as long as metresticks. Large numbers of *Triceratops* roamed the open plains of the American northwest. It was one of the last of the dinosaurs to die out.

Ankylosaurus was protected by a heavy coat of "armour." About five to six metres long and with a mass of about five tonnes, *Anky-losaurus* had triangular spines on its skull. Its armour was made of thick, bony plates set close together in a leathery skin. The plates ran the length of its body down to its rounded, clublike tail. This peaceful plant eater relied on its armour for defence.

Allosaurus was a truly fearsome hunter. It was more than nine metres long and had a mass of between three and four tonnes. A powerful runner, it covered the ground in huge strides in pursuit of its prey. Its front legs were only half as long as its hind legs; the three fingers on each front leg had sharp claws and were used for grasping.

Allosaurus had a metre-long head and a short neck. Its eyes were very large, and its eight-centimetre, knifelike teeth were notched on both edges. They could cut, saw, or rip through meat. The jaws were hinged so that a large chunk of flesh or a small animal could be swallowed whole. *Allosaurus* also fed on some of the giant plant eaters such as *Brontosaurus*.

Fossil bones of an *Allosaurus* family have been found in the western United States. Newly hatched babies were probably cared for by adults. Some scientists think that these dinosaurs even may have had "nurseries," where a few adults cared for all the young of a herd.

Archaeopteryx was the first birdlike reptile. The long feathers on its arm caused scientists to call it by a name that means "old wind." Without its feathers, *Archaeopteryx* is exactly like most small dinosaurs of that time. Yet *Archaeopteryx*'s feathers are almost identical in kind to those of birds today.

Archaeopteryx had rows of teeth, a long bony tail, and three long fingers with claws—all of which are dinosaurlike. The tail had a fringe of large feathers on either side. The five known fossils of *Archaeopteryx* were found in the limestone rocks of southern Germany.

Archaeopteryx was more of a glider and less of a flyer than the birds of today. It probably climbed trees and then launched itself into the air to catch flying insects. It may have scooped up the insects with the feathers on its arms and then used its claws to put them into its mouth. Birds today are descendants of *Archaeopteryx*.

PTEROSAURS were not, strictly speaking, dinosaurs, but were gliding reptiles related to the dinosaurs. *Pteranodon* was a giant among these animals with a huge wingspan. A specimen found in Texas had a wingspan of 15.5 m from tip to tip. With its light body and large wings, *Pteranodon* could glide for long distances, scanning the ocean waters for fish. *Pterodactyls* were similar but smaller flying reptiles. On land, all of the *PTEROSAURS* must have been clumsy and almost helpless. They became airborne simply by dropping from the edge of high cliffs.

Parasaurolophus was a dinosaur with a crest on its head. The crest, twice the length of the dinosaur's skull, was a long, bony tube that curved backward from the head like a horn. *Parasaurolophus* breathed air through the crest. The air went into the nostrils at the tip of the tube and then into the animal's lungs. Some scientists think that the crest helped to improve the animal's sense of smell.

This dinosaur was about nine metres long and had a mass of

three or four tonnes. It ate all kinds of plant materials. Besides a keen sense of smell, *Parasaurolophus* had good sight and hearing, and probably browsed in herds that were alert to any sign of danger.

The dinosaurs disappeared about 65 million years ago; no trace of them can be found after that time. But dinosaurs were not the only animals to die out then. Many other reptiles and smaller forms of life disappeared, as did many kinds of plants.

What could have caused these life forms to vanish? One theory is that a huge asteriod or comet crashed through the earth's atmosphere and struck its surface, creating an enormous crater more than 125 miles across. Some scientists believe the impact would have thrown a large cloud of dust into the sky, which would have circled the earth and blocked the sunlight for months. Temperatures would have fallen and the earth suddenly would have become much colder. Also, the dust in the air would have prevented green plants from

using sunlight to make food. Three months of darkness might have been just long enough to kill the plants and then the animals that fed on them.

Another theory is that the death of the dinosaurs resulted from a supernova explosion in a nearby star. A star exploding near our solar system would have generated a great pulse of deadly radiation that could have killed many kinds of animals and plants.

Other scientists think that dinosaurs became extinct in a much less dramatic way. They believe that the earth became gradually colder over thousands of years, and that the dinosaurs and many other animals died out because of the change in climate to which they could not adapt.

We may never know which, if any, of these theories is true. The end of the dinosaurs may always be a mystery.

HIGHWAY CONSTRUCTION
(AS EMILY DICKINSON MIGHT REACT TO IT)
by Carole Earle Chapin

Have dinosaurs come back again?
    Did you see them on my hill?
They chewed the treetops down to stump,
    Then turned indifferent heel.

Huge yellow monsters, hard to hide,
    With their prehensile mouths
Have unearthed earth, disordered it
    And unhomed every house.

Historic creatures are no more,
    I daresay these will pass:
Centuries hence, this scavenged place
    May spring again in grass!

LONG GONE
by Jack Prelutsky

Don't waste your time in looking for
the long-extinct tyrannosaur,
because this ancient dinosaur
just can't be found here anymore.

This also goes for stegosaurus,
allosaurus, brontosaurus
and any other saur or saurus
They all lived here long before us.

BRONTOSAURUS

by Gail Kredenser

The giant brontosaurus
Was a prehistoric chap
With four fat feet to stand on
And a very skimpy lap.
The scientists assure us
Of a most amazing thing—
A brontosaurus blossomed
When he had a chance to sing!

(The bigger brontosauruses,
Who liked to sing in choruses,
Would close their eyes
and harmonize
And sing most anything.)

They growled and they yowled,
They deedled and they dummed;
They warbled and they whistled,
They howled and they hummed.
They didn't eat, they didn't sleep;
They sang and sang all day.
Now all you'll find are footprints
Where they tapped the time away!

HOW THE PLAINS INDIANS LIVED

by Maria Campbell

SHELTER

The Plains Indians lived in teepees, cone-shaped tents covered with buffalo hides. A teepee was started by lashing three or four poles together with rawhide thongs; then the poles were raised to make a stand. The thongs that tied the poles together were long enough to reach the ground, where they were staked outside the teepee to provide support.

Thirteen poles or more, depending on the size wanted, were leaned counterclockwise around the stand, and covered with twelve to twenty buffalo skins which had been sewn together with sinew. This cover was drawn tightly around the poles and then pinned together with wooden pegs.

The fireplace was in the centre of the teepee, with a hole at the top for a chimney. Atop two opposite poles leaning against the teepee, flaps were attached. Moved on these poles, the flaps covered or uncovered the hole to control the heat and smoke or keep out snow.

The door faced east to greet the sun and the birth of a new day. Across from the door was the place of honour. Scattered around the floor were woven willow back rests, which were like chairs without legs. The sleeping area was covered with buffalo robes. Against the walls were containers and bags used for storing food, clothing and the personal belongings of the family.

The outside of the teepee was painted by the man of the family, either with designs given to him in a dream or vision or with pictures telling of his skills as a warrior or hunter. Near the teepee stood a pole or tripod from which hung the medicine that protected him, his home and family.

The teepees were set in a circle, the circle being a symbol of the cycle of life, and were always situated near wooded areas close to

water. Teepee poles, which were awkward to carry, might be left behind when the people moved in search of game and berries, for they always returned to the same campsites.

FOOD

The buffalo provided the plains people with their main source of food. When a herd was sighted, the medicine man of the tribe would call all the people together to dance to the Buffalo Spirit for a successful hunt. After the ceremony the hunting party would set out.

There were two main ways to take the buffalo. Before the introduction of the horse, the hunters would creep up on the herd from all sides, then rush in, simultaneously firing their arrows. With the

coming of the horse, they ran the animals down on horseback and shot their arrows on the gallop.

The second way was the jumping pound. This method was the most effective, since they could run a whole winter's supply of meat over an embankment, most often a riverbank.

CLOTHING

The Plains Indians wore clothing made from dressed hides. Preparing the hides for the clothing was a long, backbreaking process. The fresh wet hide was stretched and pegged to the ground or stretched on a rack. It was scraped clean of fat and flesh and then soaked in

a pool of water for three days or until the hair or fur began to slip off. It was stretched again and the remaining hair scraped off. After drying, the hide was rubbed with a prepared mixture of sand and animal brains, and again left to dry. In the final stage the hide was worked by rubbing it together until it was soft and pliable. Sometimes the finished product was tanned light brown or it was coloured with natural dyes.

Dyes were obtained from plants or minerals, such as iron ore for a reddish colour. From other minerals came green, blue, yellow, orange and purple. Powdered coal, charcoal and soot black were also used, as well as crushed berries and rushes. Because the Indians lived so close to nature, they observed how she blended her colours and blended theirs in the same way.

All the sewing was done with sinew, using an awl or a bone needle. The decorating of clothing was done with dyed porcupine quills and later, with dyed horsehair and beads. There is probably no finer example of quill work or the blending of natural dyes anywhere in the world.

The tails of animals such as weasels and foxes were used for decorations, as were shells, claws, feathers and hoofs. Jewellery was also made from these materials.

The plains people used body paint on special occasions such as death or sickness, and the painted designs had special significance.

buffalo
headdress

war
bonnet

The elaborate costuming that is seen today was developed only in the last hundred years with the availability of the white man's clothing and such materials as beads and dyed feathers. The ceremonial costumes worn by chicken dancers or eagle dancers were not as flamboyant as those seen today and were reserved for religious gatherings and dances, not for just any gathering.

The women wore long fringed and decorated dresses which extended from the chin to the feet. They wore knee-high leggings and moccasins. In the winter months a fur robe was also worn.

The men wore a fringed shirt, a breechcloth or a pair of aprons, and moccasins. In the winter they wore a fur robe, leggings that reached the hips, and fur-lined moccasins much higher than those worn for summer.

Blankets or robes were traditional overgarments long before the coming of the white traders. The robe, which was sometimes furred, was made pliable and soft by dressing and tanning the pelts of foxes, wolves and other animals, and sewing together the finished pelts. The buffalo robe was also prepared in this way. Sometimes fur and bird feathers were woven together to make a robe.

The Indians wore fur hats in the winter and went bareheaded in the summer. The elaborate headdresses such as war bonnets and buffalo heads were worn only by a select few and only on special occasions. Only chiefs, medicine men and those belonging to societies wore the headdresses. Warriors wore feathers, but these had to be earned by an honourable deed.

Buffalo Woman

by Paul Goble

T here was a young man already a great hunter. Even coyotes and crows and the magpies followed him to pick up scraps from his hunting. He felt a wonderful harmony with the buffalo. The people knew he could find the herds when they needed meat. When they had hunted, the young man gave thanks that the buffalo had offered themselves.

One early morning the young man went to a place at the stream where the buffalo came to drink. He waited, hidden among the bushes, watching the butterflies opening and closing their wings in the warming sun.

After a while the young man saw a buffalo cow plodding through the tall weeds toward the water. He tightened an arrow against his bowstring. The buffalo was coming very slowly.

The young man did not know whether he fell asleep, or what happened, but when he looked again the buffalo was not there. Instead, a beautiful young woman stepped from the weeds onto the pebbles at the water's edge and took a drink. She was not one of his people; her clothes were different and her hair was not braided. She smelled of wild sage and prairie flowers. He knew at once that he loved her.

"I come from the Buffalo Nation," she told him. "They have sent me because you have always had good feelings for our people. They know you are a good and kind man. I will be your wife. My people wish that the love we have for each other will be an example to both our peoples to follow."

The young man and the beautiful young woman were married. They had a son and named him Calf Boy. Their life together was good.

But the young man's relatives did not like his wife. They often said unkind things among themselves. "He has married a woman without a family," they said. "Her ways are different; she's like an animal. She will never be one of our family."

One day when the young man was away hunting, his relatives came and said to his wife: "You should never have come here; go back to wherever you came from. You are nothing but an animal, anyway." At that she immediately picked up Calf Boy and ran out of the teepee.

The young man was returning home when he saw his wife and child hurrying away from the camp. He was angry when he found out what had happened, and set out at once to bring them back.

Their trail led across rolling country. He followed all day, hearing the grasshoppers calling again and again from the sagebrush on every side. Evening was coming when he saw in the distance a painted teepee with smoke rising from a cooking fire.

The young man was surprised to see his son playing outside the teepee. When Calf Boy saw his father he ran to meet him. "I am glad you have come, Father. Mother has your meal ready." He took his father's hand and they went inside. The lodge was filled with the good smell of cooking. His wife placed a bowl of soup before him. "I am going home," she said, "I cannot live with your people. Do not follow us or you will be in great danger." "I love you," the young man said, "and wherever you and our son go, I am going too."

The young man awoke next morning looking up into the sky. The teepee was gone! There was nobody anywhere. Yet, it had not just been a dream, because he could see the circle in the dew-soaked grass where the teepee had stood, and the tracks of his wife and child leading away.

The young man followed the trail until he again came to the teepee. His son ran out to meet him.

"Mother does not want you to come any farther. Tomorrow she will make the rivers dry, but when you are thirsty, look for water in my tracks."

That evening his wife told him: "My people live beyond that distant high ridge. They know I am coming home. They are angry

because your relatives were unkind to me. Do not follow any farther or they will kill you." But the young man replied: "It does not matter when I die. I shall not turn back. I do this because I love you both."

When his wife was asleep he buckled his belt through hers and wrapped her long hair around his arm.

Again the young man awoke alone. The only tracks in the dew were those of a buffalo and her calf walking side by side. While he was wondering about the tracks, a flock of little birds flew around him excitedly: "They have gone home!" He then knew that the tracks were of his wife and child.

The tracks led toward the high ridge. Thin lines of trees marked the winding rivers. They were dry, but just as Calf Boy had told him, he found water in his hoof-prints in the baked mud of the river-beds.

From the top of the high ridge the young man looked out in wonder over the multitude of the Buffalo Nation.

As he walked down toward them a calf came running out. "Father, go back! This will kill you! Go back!"

But the young man answered: "No, Son, I shall always stay with you and Mother."

"Then you must be brave," Calf Boy said. "My Grandfather is chief of the Buffalo Nation. Do not show fear or he will surely kill you. He will ask you to find me and Mother. But you think we all look alike! When he lines us up, you will know me because I shall flick my left ear. You will find Mother because I shall put a cockle-burr on her back. You must pick us out and then you will be safe. Be attentive!"

The old bull bellowed and charged out from the herd. The ground trembled under his thundering hoofs. He stopped just in front of the young man. He pawed the earth into dust clouds, hooked his horns into clumps of sagebrush and tossed them aside in anger. The young man stood still. He showed no fear.

"Ah, this Straight-up-Person has a strong heart," breathed the old bull. "By your courage you have saved yourself. Follow me."

The old bull led the way. The silent multitude parted and joined again behind. At the centre was the painted teepee. The whole Buffalo Nation formed into radiating circles. The calves made the inner ring; the yearlings the next, the cows and bulls, all according to their ages.

"Straight-up-Person," said the old bull in a voice which all could hear, "your relatives insulted my daughter. But you have come among us because you love your wife and child. Then *find* them! If you cannot, we shall trample you until not even a stain of your blood remains."

The young man passed in front of the little calves. They looked alike, but one flicked his ear as if troubled by a fly. He laid his hand on the calf's head. "My Son," he said, and a sound of surprise came from the multitude. "This must be a wonderful Person," they said.

He then walked around the circle formed by the cows. Again, they all looked alike, but he came to one with a cockle-burr on her back; "My Wife," he said. Once more a sound of surprise came from the Buffalo Nation: "Ah, he calls her 'wife'."

"This Straight-up-Person loves his wife and little child," the old bull announced. "He was willing to die for them. We shall make him one of us. We shall all join in with our thoughts while we do this."

The young man was led inside the teepee and they tied the door shut. His only covering was a buffalo robe with the horns and hoofs attached.

For three days and nights the buffalo surrounded the teepee filling the air with their continuous grunts and bellowing.

On the fourth day the bulls made a sudden rush and pushed the teepee over. They rolled and rolled the young man in a wallow until he was covered all over with dirt. They squeezed the breath from his body and breathed new breath into him. They licked him and rubbed against him until his man-smell was gone. He tried to stand but he could not. He felt the robe become a part of him. When the bulls heard him grunting they worked even harder, tumbling him over and over.

And at last, he stood up on his own four legs — a young buffalo bull. That was a wonderful day! The relationship was made between the People and the Buffalo Nation; it will last until the end of time.

It will be remembered that a brave young man became a buffalo because he loved his wife and little child. In return the Buffalo People have given their flesh so that little children, and babies still unborn, will always have meat to eat. It is the Creator's wish.

Mitakuye oyasin — We are all related.

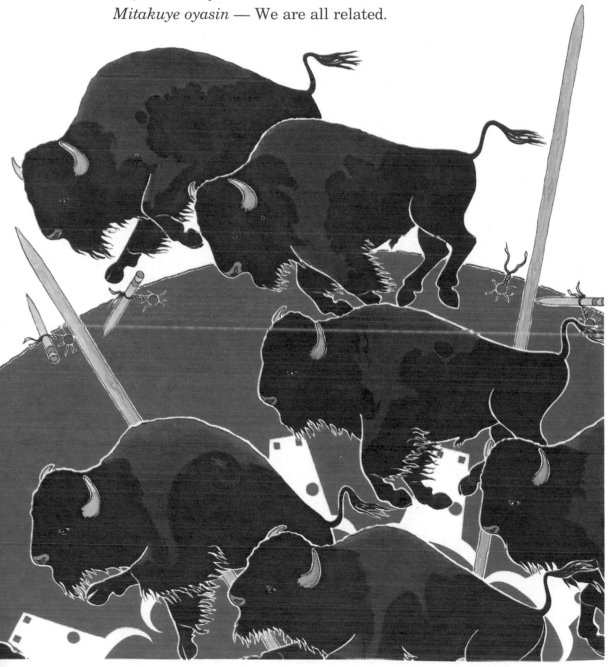

THE BONE GATHERERS

by David Booth

Sod-busters arrived on the prairies
after the buffalo had gone.
The homesteaders gambled against
drought
insects
hailstones
heat
starvation.
But
buffalo butchers had taken the life-source.
And in the wheel tracks of the skinners,
the late-comers gathered
bones and horns
(bones at eight dollars a ton,
horns at twelve)
which became bone china, or buttons or eyeglasses
in the hands of the easterners.

The old weathered bones were ground into bonemeal
for fertilizer
and the buffalo returned to the earth.

RED RIVER CART SONG

by *Lorraine Johnson*

The railhead was in Calgary back in those early days.
And everyone a-goin' north had to find a different way.
There were horses dragging travois, they had been there
   from the start.
But my father went to Edmonton in a Red River cart.

The only road the prairies knew was called the Calgary Trail,
For horses, mules and oxen, and the men who carried mail,
For families from the east who came for a new start.
And my father went to Edmonton in a Red River cart.

The families filled the prairies when the land was fresh and new.
The sky went on forever while the population grew.
They built cities and farms, those people did their part.
And my father went to Edmonton in a Red River cart.

Roll along the prairies, you great big wooden wheels.
Stir the dust and fill the air with screeching and with squeals,
Pitch and sway from side to side, the summer day is long,
And make your way up north, singing the Red River Cart Song.

from

LITTLE HOUSE ON THE PRAIRIE

by Laura Ingalls Wilder

A long time ago, when all the grandfathers and grandmothers of today were little boys and little girls or very small babies, or perhaps not even born, Pa and Ma and Mary and Laura and Baby Carrie left their little house in the Big Woods of Wisconsin. They drove away and left it lonely and empty in the clearing among the big trees, and they never saw that little house again.

They were going to the Indian country.

Pa said there were too many people in the Big Woods now. Quite often Laura heard the ringing thud of an ax which was not Pa's ax, or the echo of a shot that did not come from his gun. The path that went by the little house had become a road. Almost every day Laura and Mary stopped their playing and stared in surprise at a wagon slowly creaking by on that road.

Wild animals would not stay in a country where there were so many people. Pa did not like to stay, either. He liked a country where the wild animals lived without being afraid. He like to see the little fawns and their mothers looking at him from the shadowy woods, and the fat, lazy bears eating berries in the wild-berry patches.

In the long winter evenings he talked to Ma about the Western country. In the West the land was level, and there were no trees. The grass grew thick and high. There the wild animals wandered and fed as though they were in a pasture that stretched much farther than a man could see, and there were no settlers. Only Indians lived there.

One day in the very last of the winter Pa said to Ma, "Seeing you don't object, I've decided to go see the West. I've had an offer for this place, and we can sell it now for as much as we're ever likely to get, enough to give us a start in a new country."

"Oh, Charles, must we go now?" Ma said. The weather was so cold and the snug house was so comfortable.

"If we're going this year, we must go now," said Pa. "We can't get across the Mississippi after the ice breaks."

So Pa sold the little house. He sold the cow and calf. He made hickory bows and fastened them upright to the wagon box. Ma helped him stretch white canvas over them.

In the thin dark before morning Ma gently shook Mary and Laura till they got up. In firelight and candlelight she washed and combed them and dressed them warmly. Over their long red-flannel underwear she put wool petticoats and wool dresses and long wool stockings. She put their coats on them, and their rabbit-skin hoods and their red yarn mittens.

Everything from the little house was in the wagon, except the beds and tables and chairs. They did not need to take these, because Pa could always make new ones.

There was thin snow on the ground. The air was still and cold and dark. The bare trees stood up against the frosty stars. But in the east the sky was pale and through the grey woods came lanterns with wagons and horses, bringing Grandpa and aunts and uncles and cousins.

Mary and Laura clung tight to their rag dolls and did not say anything. The cousins stood around and looked at them. Grandma and all the aunts hugged and kissed them and hugged and kissed them again, saying goodbye.

Pa hung his gun to the wagon bows inside the canvas top, where he could reach it quickly from the seat. He hung his bullet-pouch and powder-horn beneath it. He laid the fiddle-box carefully between pillows, where jolting would not hurt the fiddle.

The uncles helped him hitch the horses to the wagon. All the cousins were told to kiss Mary and Laura, so they did. Pa picked up Mary and then Laura, and set them on the bed in the back of the wagon. He helped Ma climb up to the wagon seat, and Grandma reached and gave her Baby Carrie. Pa swung up and sat beside Ma, and Jack, the brindle bulldog, went under the wagon.

So they all went away from the little log house. The shutters were over the windows, so the little house could not see them go. It stayed there inside the log fence, behind the two big oak trees that in the summertime had made green roofs for Mary and Laura to play under. And that was the last of the little house.

Pa promised that when they came to the West, Laura should see a papoose.

"What is a papoose?" she asked him, and he said, "A papoose is a little, brown, Indian baby."

They drove a long way through the snowy woods, till they came to the town of Pepin. Mary and Laura had seen it once before, but it looked different now. The door of the store and the doors of all the houses were shut, the stumps were covered with snow, and no little children were playing outdoors. Big cords of wood stood among the stumps. Only two or three men in boots and fur caps and bright plaid coats were to be seen.

Ma and Laura and Mary ate bread and molasses in the wagon, and the horses ate corn from nosebags, while inside the store Pa traded his furs for things they would need on the journey. They could not stay long in the town, because they must cross the lake that day.

The enormous lake stretched flat and smooth and white all the way to the edge of the grey sky. Wagon tracks went away across it, so far that you could not see where they went; they ended in nothing at all.

Pa drove the wagon out onto the ice, following those wagon

tracks. The horses' hoofs clop-clopped with a dull sound, the wagon wheels went crunching. The town grew smaller and smaller behind, till even the tall store was only a dot. All around the wagon there was nothing but empty and silent space. Laura didn't like it. But Pa was on the wagon seat and Jack was under the wagon; she knew that nothing could hurt her while Pa and Jack were there.

At last the wagon was pulling up a slope of earth again, and again there were trees. There was a little log house, too, among the trees. So Laura felt better.

Nobody lived in the little house; it was a place to camp in. It was a tiny house, and strange, with a big fireplace and rough bunks against all the walls. But it was warm when Pa had built a fire in the fireplace. That night Mary and Laura and Baby Carrie slept with Ma in a bed made on the floor before the fire, while Pa slept outside in the wagon, to guard it and the horses.

In the night a strange noise awakened Laura. It sounded like a shot, but it was sharper and longer than a shot. Again and again she heard it. Mary and Carrie were asleep, but Laura couldn't sleep until Ma's voice came softly through the dark.

"Go to sleep, Laura," Ma said. " It's only the ice cracking."

Next morning Pa said, "It's lucky we crossed yesterday, Caroline. Wouldn't wonder if the ice broke up today. We made a late crossing, and we're lucky it didn't start breaking up while we were out in the middle of it."

"I thought about that yesterday, Charles," Ma replied, gently.

Laura hadn't thought about it before, but now she thought what would have happened if the ice had cracked under the wagon wheels and they had all gone down into the cold water in the middle of that vast lake.

"You're frightening somebody, Charles," Ma said, and Pa caught Laura up in his safe, big hug.

"We're across the Mississippi!" he said, hugging her joyously.

A LETTER FROM THE COAST

by Laura Ingalls Wilder

Laura Ingalls Wilder, the author of Little House on the Prairie, *went to visit her daughter, Rose, in San Francisco during the summer of 1915. Canada and Britain were at war with Germany at that time. (The United States entered the war in 1917.) In this letter to her husband, Almonzo, Laura describes San Francisco Bay.*

San Francisco
September 13, 1915

Manly Dear,

I am perched on the side of Telegraph Hill watching the ships go by. There are twenty-six ships in sight and ten small sail boats. One of them is a hay boat. It looks like a load of hay floating on the water with three sails on it. There are about three thousand tons of hay on board, one thousand down below decks and the two thousand on deck. It looks strange to see a load of hay floating on the water. It has come down some river from the alfalfa farms. Just now a British trading ship is going past outward bound, perhaps to be sunk by a German submarine. It is the freight steamers, you know, that they particularly want to get. It has gone past now and I hear the blast of its whistle. I suppose it is meeting some other ship. Now in the immediate foreground is a white ferry steamer and farther over an orange-coloured Exposition ferry bound for the Exposition grounds. There are two lumber ships going by loaded with lumber. One of

them is coming into the pier. It is loaded a little unevenly and tips some to one side. I suppose it lists to starboard or to larboard or something. One sailing ship with dirty-looking sails with clean new patches on them has sailed in and dropped anchor. The sails are running down. Now someone is getting over the side into a little boat. This ship looks like a tramp and I think it is. A ship is going by now that came from the Hawaiian Islands with a cargo of sugar. It is empty and riding high in the water. A Hawaiian passenger ship has passed bound for the Hawaiian Islands and Uncle Sam's grey battleship is lying anchored a little way out. Little white yachts are scurrying among the larger ships. There are six piers in sight with all kinds of ships tied up to them. One is a British freighter with a flag flying, glad to be safe for awhile, I suppose. Another is a Greek ship with several strings of flags flying in the winds. They say that is a sign that it will leave soon.

The hills across the bay look beautiful through the fog and Berkeley and Oakland show dimly. The tide is rising now and pouring in through the Golden Gate. I can see just how far it has come in by the white caps on the water. Goat Island is right in front. That is where the naval training school is.

One little sailing boat has just gone by, sailing so close into the wind that the tip of the sail touches the water now and then. The man in sight is standing on the other edge of the boat, out on the very edge to keep it from tipping over. But I could watch these ships go by and write you about them all day. Rose is thinking of moving out here. There is a little house she can rent which faces all this. It is built on the side of the hill and there is a balcony overhanging the steep hillside. It looks over the roofs of the houses below, and the piers and all the beautiful bay is spread out like a picture. An artist friend of Rose's, a dear girl, is moving into another little house right next to the one Rose can get. The places are rather dilapidated but can be fixed very cozily.

I am glad Inky is more cheerful and that you are getting along all right. Rose and I are going to do some work on stories together this week.

Lovingly,
Bessie

I forgot to say that there is a wireless station on Goat Island. I can see the mast. From there they talk to Honolulu in the Hawaiian Islands. I saw a yacht race this afternoon too. Twenty-one little sail boats with their white sails filling out with the wind came into sight like a flock of white ducks. They sailed to a certain point, then turned and raced back out of sight behind the headland. It was very pretty.

from

THAT SCATTERBRAIN BOOKY

by Bernice Thurman Hunter

Yonge Street hummed and sparkled in the early spring sunshine. Cars honked and horses whinnied. Dogs barked, bicycle bells jangled and the popcorn man's whistle blew a long thin note.

I read all the signboards as we passed. "Smoke Sweet Caporal," "Buy British Consul" and "Drink Coca-Cola." Boy, how I'd love to drink Coca-Cola. I had no idea what it tasted like, but the beautiful girl on the billboard said, "It's delicious!"

"I love Yonge Street, don't you, Mum?"

"Yes," she said, chewing a Brazil nut with her front teeth because the back ones had been bothering her lately. "And did you know, Bea, that it's the longest street in the world?"

"I didn't know that, Mum!"

"Well, you learn something every day."

Helen Hayes and Clark Gable were in a talkie at Loew's Theatre. I hadn't seen a talking picture yet, but Mum said when she had enough money she'd take me.

"Ka-ween Street!" bellowed the conductor. "Eaton's! Simpson's! Have your fares ready. This way out!" He pulled a lever by the fare box and the double doors clunked open. We jostled our way to the sidewalk.

Woolworth's Five-and-Ten-Cent Store stood on the corner of Queen and Yonge. And huddled in the swinging doorway was Old Blind Bill (that's what the sign said that hung around his neck).

"I'm sorry, Bill," Mum murmured as we passed.

"I didn't know you knew Blind Bill, Mum," I said.

"Shush, Bea," she said, "I only know him to see."

Toronto's two biggest department stores faced each other across Queen Street: the T. Eaton Company on the north and the Robert Simpson Company on the south. A steady stream of shoppers dodged each other to get to the opposite side. But Mum and I never went to Simpson's because Mum was a dyed-in-the-wool Eatonian.

We squeezed into the revolving doors together and let ourselves be swept inside. Then we stopped at the foot of Timothy Eaton's statue to wait for Aunt Hester, Uncle William's wife.

It was sort of a custom to meet at the store-founder's monument. And while you waited you gave his big bronze toe a rub for good luck. Mum said that was silly superstition, but she gave the shiny spot a quick little pat just in case.

"I remember the day he was buried," she mused, looking up into the bearded bronze face. "I was just a little bit of a thing and Poppa put me up on his shoulders so I could see. I can still feel the hush that fell over the crowd as the hearse went by. And following it came hundreds of carriages, all draped in black."

I love to hear stories of the olden days. But before Mum had a chance to say any more we saw Aunt Hester bouncing towards us between the counters, her curls bobbing like little gold springs around her face.

Mum was a bit jealous of Aunt Hester. "She's got neither chick nor child and more money than she knows what to do with," she sighed enviously.

I knew this was true because I heard Mum tell Dad once that Uncle William brought home sixteen dollars every single week.

"Hello there, Tinker!" cried Aunt Hester breathlessly. She always called me Tinker.

The two of them had a little chat, then we made our way down the stairs and through the underground tunnel to the Annex. The tunnel ran under Albert Street. It always smelled of paint and turpentine. It was kind of a nice smell.

We stopped to watch a man demonstrate some cleaning fluid. First he smeared black grease on a patch of carpet. Then he removed it, clean as a whistle, with his magic cleaner. Aunt Hester got carried away and bought a large bottle for fifty cents.

The Annex was Eaton's bargain store. Its basement was a dank, smelly place with low-hanging pipes and uneven, littered wood floors. Mum hated the Annex. She said if Dad ever got working steady again it wouldn't see her for dust.

The basement was crowded, as usual, with crabby, frazzled mothers and whiny, dirty-nosed kids. Mountains of dry goods were piled up on big square tables. Mum stopped at every table to pick things over. Aunt Hester bought Uncle William a set of long drawers for ninety-nine cents and two pairs of socks for a quarter.

"If I had your money, Hester," Mum said, watching her sister-in-law peel off a two-dollar bill from a fat wad, "I wouldn't come near this place. I'd stick to the Main Store where everything is first class. Just look at this stuff, all soiled and messy." She flicked at the second-class goods disdainfully.

"There's not a thing wrong with these socks," replied Aunt Hester indignantly. "And my Thor will take out the spots in these drawers in the very first wash."

Mum winced at the mention of the Thor. I thought how dumb it was that Aunt Hester, with neither chick nor child, should own a washing machine while Mum, with all us kids, had to scrub on the wash-board.

Mum was holding up a corselet, eyeing it critically. The flesh-coloured garment had two huge scoops in the front. I looked down at my flat chest and couldn't even imagine fitting into such a thing.

By this time my legs were killing me, so I hung onto the table edge and let them go all limp. It felt good. At last they got sick of underwear and we headed for the shoe department.

The minute I laid eyes on them I knew I had to have them. They were black patent leather with white patent bows and they were absolutely gorgeous. I could see myself in Sunday School swinging my feet out for Mr. Henderson, the Superintendent, to see.

Mum was paying a lot of attention to a pair of sturdy brown oxfords, so I grabbed the patents and shoved them under her nose.

"Please, Mum, can I have these?" I begged. "I promise I won't run in them, and I'll take them off after four every day."

"Oh, pshaw, Bea." She was smiling so I knew I had a chance. "You're too much of a scatterbrain to remember not to run. You'd have those flimsy slippers scuffed out in no time."

"No, Mum, I wouldn't! I'm not a scatterbrain!" For the first time

I really resented the silly nickname. "I won't run — honest — I'll walk slow and careful all the time."

"Perhaps the young lady would like to try them on," came a man's silky voice from behind. The shoe salesman looked for all the world like the picture of Warner Baxter stuck up on our bedroom wall.

Mum didn't speak quickly enough, and before she knew it, he was down on his knees slipping them on my feet.

In spite of my brown ribbed stockings wrinkling around my ankles, the shoes looked beautiful. I got up and began to strut to show them off. I guess I looked unusually pleased with myself because Mum gave in sooner than I dared to hope.

"How much are they?" she asked Warner Baxter.

"They're a terrific buy at fifty cents," he assured her. "Only last week they were selling for ninety-cents and going like hotcakes. This is my last pair, an Opportunity Day special."

"Are you sure they fit, Bea?" Mum said. "They're final clearance so we can't bring them back, you know."

"I'm sure, Mum," I said.

"All right then." She couldn't resist a genuine bargain. And the price tickled her pink. Seeing she was in such a good mood, I begged to wear them home. She said that I could if I promised not to scuff them. Warner Baxter wrapped up my old shoes and handed me the package.

From the shoe department we went straight to the Annex lunch counter. It was a stand-up counter with no stools. Aunt Hester treated herself and Mum to a red-hot and a Vernor's and they both shared them with me. First I had a bite of Mum's red-hot, then a bite of Aunt Hester's. I watched a bit worriedly as the level of the sparkling drink crept lower in their glasses. They were chatting and sipping and seeming to pay no attention to me. But they both remembered to save me the last long slurp at the end.

After that we went to the Main Store, just looking. Instead of the elevators, we rode the moving stairs because Mum knew I liked them best. I always got an excited, scary feeling as we curved over

the top and the moving stairs disappeared beneath our feet. Arthur told me once about a boy who got sucked in by his shoelaces and ended up a pile of mincemeat. But that couldn't happen to me today because my new shoes were slip-ons.

By the time we were on our way home, my feet were killing me. I knew five minutes after I put them on that my beautiful patent-leather slippers were at least two sizes too small.

"How do your new shoes feel, Bea?" Mum asked as we stepped off the streetcar. She must have read my mind!

"Just fine, Mum." My face turned beet-red with the big fat lie, but she didn't seem to notice.

JINGLES

Zeenty, teenty, feggerie fell,
    Pompaleerie jig.
Every man who has no hair
    Generally wears a wig.

Spring is showery, flowery, bowery;
Summer: hoppy, croppy, poppy;
Autumn: wheezy, sneezy, freezy;
Winter: slippy, drippy, nippy.

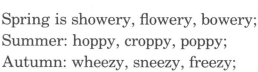

Hink, minx! the old witch winks,
    The fat begins to fry:
There's nobody at home but little jumping Joan,
    Father, Mother, and I.

I asked my mother for fifteen cents
To see the elephant jump the fence,
He jumped so high that he touched the sky
And never came back 'till the first of July.

How much wood would a wood-chuck chuck
If a wood-chuck could chuck wood?
He would chuck as much wood as a wood-chuck would chuck,
If a wood-chuck could chuck wood.

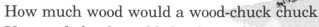

Bat, bat
　　Come under my hat,
　　And I'll give you a slice of bacon;
And when I bake,
I'll give you a cake,
　　If I am not mistaken.

"Fire! Fire!"
Said Mrs. McGuire.
"Where, Where?"
Said Mrs. Ware.
"Downtown!"
Said Mrs. Brown.
"Heaven save us!"
Said Mrs. Davis.

What's in the cupboard?
Says Mr. Hubbard.
A knuckle of veal,
Says Mr. Beal.
Is that all?
Says Mr. Ball.
And enough too,
Says Mr. Glue;
And away they all flew.

There were three ghostesses
Sitting on postesses
Eating buttered toastesses
And greasing their fistesses
Right up to their wristesses.
Weren't they beastesses
To make such feastesses!

ONE DAY AFTER

What does tomorrow hold in store for us? We don't really know, do we? We can dream about the future, and hope about good things to come, but we will have to wait one day at a time. Writers enjoy creating imaginary tomorrows for us to wonder about, making up strange places and impossible events. Just read this next excerpt, where some rats are learning to read!

The one important phase of training began one day after weeks of really hard work at the "shape recognition" that I mentioned before. But this was different. For the first time they used sounds along with the shapes, and pictures, real pictures we could recognize. For example, one of the first and simplest of these exercises was a picture, a clear photograph, of a rat. I suppose they felt sure we would know what that was. This picture was shown on a screen, with a light behind it. Then, after I had looked at the picture and recognized it, a shape flashed on the screen under it — a sort of half circle and two straight lines, not like anything I had seen before. Then the voice began:

"Are."

"Are."

"Are."

It was Julie's voice, speaking very clearly, but it had a tinny sound — it was a record. After repeating "are" a dozen times or so, that particular shape disappeared and another one came on the screen, still under the picture of the rat. It was a triangle,

with legs on it. And Julie's voice began again:

"Aiee."

"Aiee."

"Aiee."

When that shape disappeared a third one came on the screen. This one was a cross. Julie's voice said:

"Tea."

"Tea."

"Tea."

Then all three shapes appeared at once, and the record said:

"Are."

"Aiee."

"Tea."

"Rat."

You will have already recognized what was going on: they were teaching us to read. The symbols under the picture were the letters R-A-T. But the idea did not become clear to me, nor to any of us, for quite a long time. Because, of course, we didn't know what reading was.

(from *Mrs. Frisby and the Rats of NIMH*, by Robert C. O'Brien)

This is an imaginary experiment, but there are many real ones being done today with animals and, of course, with humans. Think of the astronauts working in outer space!

The selections in this section will make you think about the future. What will happen one day after today?

ROBOTS

by Paula Taylor

ROBOTS IN THE OFFICE

Tomorrow's offices will also have their share of robot workers. One robot that's already on the job is the Mailmobile. It moves slowly through large office buildings, carrying letters, packages, and supplies. At each stop, it pauses for 20 seconds so people can come and get their mail. Then it gives a warning beep and moves on. The Mailmobile follows an invisible chemical path which is sprayed on the carpet. An ultraviolet light underneath the robot makes the pathway glow, and a light sensor guides the machine along the track.

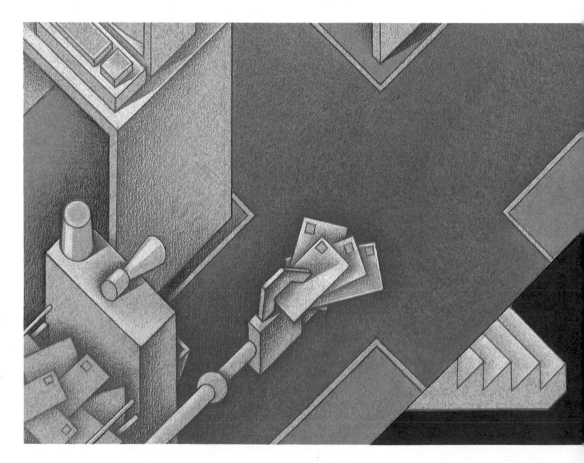

HOMEMADE ROBOTS

When will we have mechanical servants who can be programmed to do household chores automatically? Most computer experts think it may take another fifty years or more to develop robots with this much skill and intelligence. But the experts may be wrong. In basements and garages all across the country amateur robot-makers are hard at work. They're turning odd assortments of tin cans, computers, car batteries, and plastic domes into intelligent machines — robots that can speak, understand words, and find their way around the house. These homemade robots may speed the development of machines that are skillful enough to work around the house and smart enough to act as nursemaids and companions. Before we know it, all of us may be living with machines that have minds of their own.

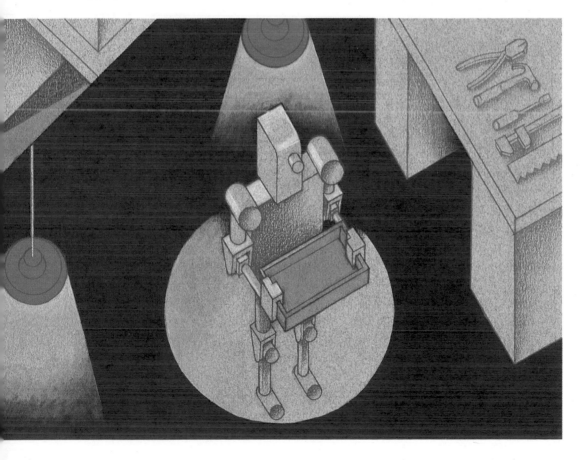

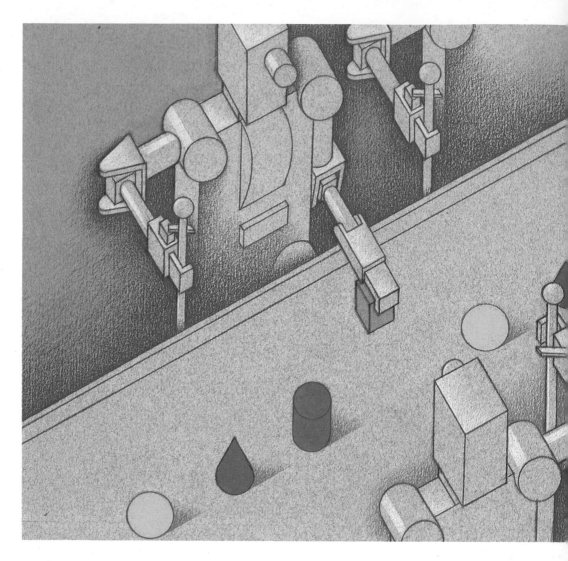

ROBOTS IN THE FACTORY

In factories of the future, workers will do their jobs quickly, without making a single mistake. They'll never be bored, even when they have to do the same job over and over again. They'll work all day and all night, without ever stopping to rest. Impossible? Not when the workers are robots.

Today, robots are already taking over many factory jobs which are dangerous, difficult — or just plain boring. They move metal parts which are too hot or too heavy for people to handle. They work in places which are hot or dusty or noisy or filled with poisonous fumes or gases. Most factory robots have one long arm with a flexible

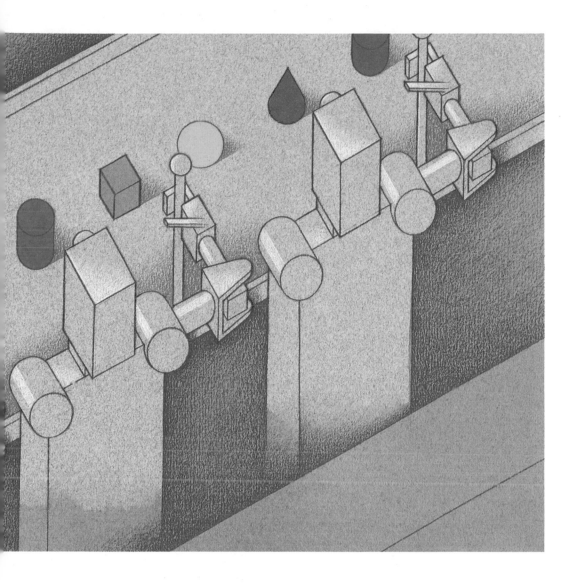

"wrist" and a claw "hand." They can be programmed to do many different tasks. To teach a robot what to do, a human worker slowly leads its arm and hand through the series of movements required for its job. The robot "remembers" these motions. It will repeat them over and over until someone erases its memory and gives it new orders.

Today, robots have to be programmed and repaired by human workers. But soon even this work may be done by other robots. Someday it may be possible for factories to operate without any humans at all.

TOMORROW

by Martin Charnin

The sun'll come out tomorrow,
bet your bottom dollar
that tomorrow there'll be sun!

Jus' thinking about tomorrow
clears away the cobwebs and the sorrow
till there's none.

When I'm stuck with a day that's grey and lonely,
I just stick out my chin and grin and say:

Oh! The sun'll come out tomorrow
So you got to hang on till tomorrow
come what may.

Tomorrow, tomorrow,
I love ya tomorrow,
you're always a day away!

Tomorrow, tomorrow,
I love ya tomorrow,
you're only a day away.

from
THE IRON MAN
by Ted Hughes

The Iron Man came to the top of the cliff.

How far had he walked? Nobody knows. Where had he come from? Nobody knows. How was he made? Nobody knows.

Taller than a house, the Iron Man stood at the top of the cliff, on the very brink, in the darkness.

The wind sang through his iron fingers. His great iron head, shaped like a dustbin but as big as a bedroom slowly turned to the right, slowly turned to the left. His iron ears turned this way, that way. He was hearing the sea. His eyes, like headlamps, glowed white, then red, then infra-red, searching the sea. Never before had Iron Man seen the sea.

He swayed in the strong wind that pressed against his back. He swayed forward, on the brink of the high cliff.

And his right foot, his enormous iron right foot, lifted — up, out, into space, and the Iron Man stepped forward, off the cliff, into nothingness.

CRRRAAAASSSSSSH!

Down the cliff the Iron Man came toppling, head over heels.

CRASH!

CRASH!

CRASH!

From rock to rock, snag to snag, tumbling slowly. And as he crashed and crashed and crashed

His iron legs fell off.

His iron arms broke off, and the hands broke off the arms.

His great iron head fell off.

All the separate pieces tumbled, scattered, crashing, bumping, clanging, down onto the rocky beach far below.

A few rocks tumbled with him.

Then

Silence.

Only the sound of the sea, chewing away at the edge of the

rocky beach, where the bits and pieces of the Iron Man lay scattered far and wide, silent and unmoving.

Only one of the iron hands, lying beside an old, sandlogged washed-up seaman's boat, waved its fingers for a minute, like a crab on its back. Then it lay still.

While the stars went on wheeling through the sky and the wind went on tugging at the grass on the cliff-top and the sea went on boiling and booming.

Nobody knew the Iron Man had fallen.

Night passed.

Just before dawn, as the darkness grew blue and the shapes of the rocks separated from each other, two seagulls flew crying over the rocks. They landed on a patch of sand. They had two chicks in a nest on the cliff. Now they were searching for food.

One of the seagulls flew up — Aaaaaark! He had seen something. He glided low over the sharp rocks. He landed and picked something up. Something shiny, round and hard. It was one of Iron Man's eyes. He brought it back to his mate. They both looked at this strange thing. And the eye looked at them. It rolled from side to side looking first at one gull, then at the other. The gulls, peering at it, thought it was a strange kind of clam, peeping at them from its shell.

Then the other gull flew up, wheeled around and landed and picked something up. Some awkward, heavy thing. Finally, the gull dropped it beside the eye. This new thing had five legs. It moved. The gulls thought it was a strange kind of crab. They did not know they had found the Iron Man's eye and the Iron Man's right hand.

But as soon as the eye and the hand got together the eye looked at the hand. Its light glowed blue. The hand stood up on three fingers and its thumb, and craned its forefinger like a long nose. It felt around. It touched the eye. Gleefully it picked up the eye, and tucked it under its middle finger. The eye peered out, between the forefinger and thumb. Now the hand could see.

It looked around. Then it darted and jabbed one of the gulls with its stiffly held finger, then darted at the other and jabbed him.

The two gulls flew up into the wind with a frightened cry.

Slowly then the hand crept over the stones, searching. It ran forward suddenly, grabbed something and tugged. But the thing was stuck between two rocks. The thing was one of the Iron Man's arms. At last the hand left the arm and went scuttling hither and thither among the rocks, till it stopped, and touched something gently. This thing was the other hand. This new hand stood up and hooked its finger round the little finger of the hand with the eye, and let itself be led. Now the two hands, the seeing one leading the blind one, walking on their finger tips, went back together to the arm, and together they tugged it free. The hand with the eye fastened itself onto the wrist of the arm. The arm stood up and walked on its hand. The other hand clung on behind as before, and this strange trio went searching.

An eye! There it was, blinking at them speechlessly beside a black and white pebble. The seeing hand fitted the eye to the blind hand and now both hands could see. They went running among the rocks. Soon they found a leg. They jumped on top of the leg and the leg went hopping over the rocks with the arm swinging from the hand that clung to the top of the leg. The other hand clung on top of that hand. The two hands, with their eyes, guided the leg, twisting it this way and that, as a rider guides a horse.

Soon they found another leg and the other arm. Now each hand, with an eye under its palm and an arm dangling from its wrist, rode on a leg separately about the beach. Hop, hop, hop, they went, peering among the rocks. One found an ear and at the same moment the other found the giant torso. Then the busy hands fitted the legs to the torso, then they fitted the arms, each fitting the other, and the torso stood up with legs and arms but no head. It walked about the beach, holding its eyes up in its hands, searching for its lost head. At last, there was the head — eyeless, earless, nested in a heap of red seaweed. Now in no time the Iron Man had fitted his head back, and his eyes were in place, and everything in place except for one ear. He strode about the beach searching for his lost ear, as the sun rose over the sea and the day came.

The two gulls sat on their ledge, high on the cliff. They watched the immense man striding to and fro over the rocks below. Between them, on the nesting ledge, lay a great iron ear. The gulls could not eat it. The baby gulls could not eat it. There it lay on the high ledge.

Far below, the Iron Man searched.

At last he stopped, and looked at the sea. Was he thinking the sea had stolen his ear? Perhaps he was thinking the sea had come up, while he lay scattered, and had gone down again with his ear.

He walked towards the sea. He walked into the breakers, and there he stood for a while, the breakers bursting around his knees.

Then he walked in deeper, deeper, deeper.

The gulls took off and glided down low over the great iron head that was now moving slowly out through the swell. The eyes blazed red, level with the wave tops, till a big wave covered them and foam spouted over the top of the head. The head still moved out under water. The eyes and the top of the head appeared for a moment in a hollow of the swell. Now the eyes were green. Then the sea covered them and the head.

The gulls circled low over the line of bubbles that went on moving slowly out into the deep sea.

Moon Poem

by Saundra Sharp

"Ouu
gee whiz
hey charlie
look
purple rocks
hey alan
over here
looks like glass
got to have
one of these
just like green glass
ouu get one of those . . . ."

You'all better leave God's moon alone,
Else he ain't gonna turn it on, no more!

TELL ME A STORY
by *Eve Merriam*

Tell me a story
of eons ago
when the world was not
the world we know:

when dinosaurs roamed
and reptiles flew
and four-footed animals
upright grew.

Now tell me a story
of women and men
living on the moon —
and what happens then.

FUTURE STORY

by *Fiona French*

∘∘∘ The year is 2301. A mysterious alien signal is received on Earth and an expedition sent to investigate. Photon Starship SPECTRA 3 will travel near the speed of light towards the star Epsilon Eridani. She carries a crew of two men and one woman into the vast unknown of outer space ∘∘∘

PHOTON STARSHIP SPECTRA 3 □□ MISSION

▷ Investigate alien distress call ∘∘∘ Unidentified radio source – Narvis ◁ Earth departure ▷ 9 May 2301 ... Distance ▷ 10.75 Light years ... Speed ▷ 70% Speed of light ... Course ▷ Epsilon Eridani / Alien radio sour ... Arrival Narvis ▷ 7 October 2316 ...

SPECTRA 3 □□ STARSHIP CREW DATA

Commander Hersch
Home planet ▷ Earth
Exobiologist
Age ▷ 30

Astronaut Cass
Home planet ▷ Earth
Geophysicist
Age ▷ 32

Astronaut Low
Home planet ▷ Mercury
Astrophysicist
Age ▷ 32

Crew Life Support System ▷ Activated/Functioning

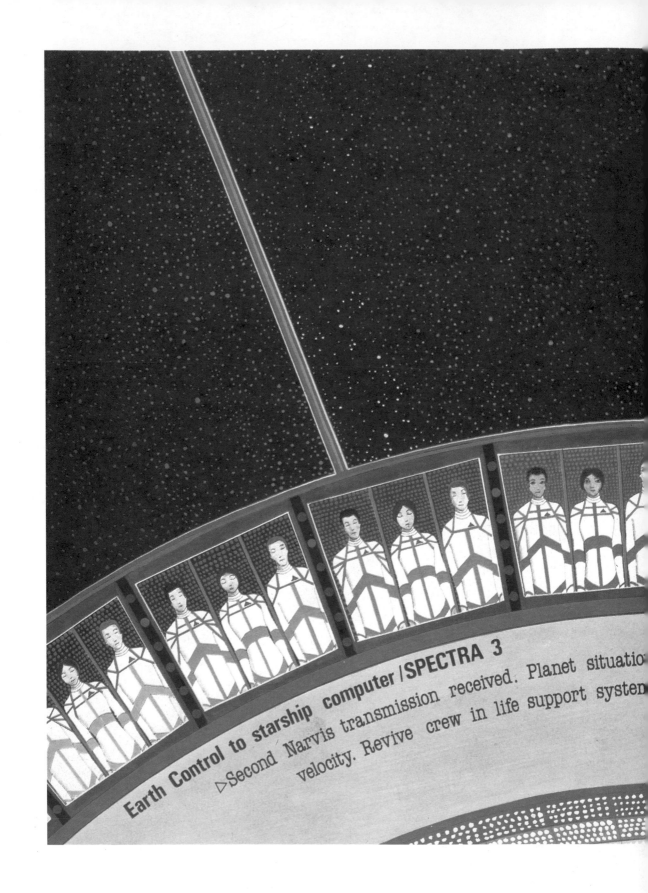

Earth Control to starship computer /SPECTRA 3
▷Second Narvis transmission received. Planet situatio...
velocity. Revive crew in life support system...

ritical. Native life-forms dying. Increase to maximum ⊲ rgent you reach Narvis. ⊲ **Transmission ends.**

Arrival Narvis ⊳ 15 November 2312 ...
Speed ⊳ 90% speed of light

SPECTRA 3 to Earth / 15 November 2312 / Astronaut Low reporting

▷We haven't picked up any signals from the planet. Radio reception is dead. There is no trace of life on Narvis from up here. Hersch and Cass will take landing craft to investigate planet surface.◁

"No sign of life here. We are bringing a crystal back to the ship."

SPECTRA 3 to Earth

▷All astronauts aboard starship. There is no life left on Narvis. Repeat—No life on Narvis. We are returning to Earth.◁

SPECTRA 3 to Earth ... EMERGENCY...
▷ Electromagnetic storm has activated the crystal
from Narvis. Starship guidance
system inoperative. Repeat —
Starship out of control ₀₀₀

SPECTRA 3 to Earth ...»S.O.S.»...»S.O.S.»...»S.O.S.»...»S.O.S.»...
▷Starship turning into crystal. Maintaining maximum speed.
Re-entry into Earth atmosphere in forty-eight hours. Communication system
is crystallizing.◁ **Transmission ends.**

SPECTRA 3 □□ LOCATION ANALYSIS
Atmospheric Contents ▷ Nitrogen 78.08% ⋯ Oxygen 20.95% ⋯
Argon 0.93% ⋯ Carbon dioxide 0.03% ⋯ Neon 0.002%
Humidity ▷7 g/m³ ⋯ Temperature ▷15° C

Earth Control to SPECTRA 3
▷Welcome home ∘∘∘ Welcome home ∘∘∘

ZACHARY ZED

by James Reeves

Zachary Zed was the last man,
    The last man left on earth.
For everyone else had died but him
    And no more come to birth.

In former times young Zachary
    Had asked a maid to wed.
"I loves thee, dear," he told her true,
    "Will thou be Missis Zed?"

"No, not if you was the last man
    On earth!" the maid replied:
And he was; but she wouldn't give consent,
    And in due time she died.

So all alone stood Zachary.
    "'Tis not so bad," he said,
"There's no one to make me brush my hair
    Nor send me up to bed.

"There's none can call me wicked,
    Nor none to argufy,
So dang my soul if I don't per-nounce
    LONG LIVE KING ZACHAR — Y!"

So Zachary Zed was the last man
    And the last king beside,
And never a person lived to tell
    If ever Zachary died.

U.F.O.

by Joanna Stubbs

A million million stars glittered against the blackness of the sky like spilt salt.

Oj the shepherd boy was counting them that night to keep himself awake when a shooting star fell. And fell. And went on falling, instead of vanishing as shooting stars should, until it was a whirling bright egg of light spinning down and looking as if it must surely fall onto the castle.

Oj ran to tell the king.

The people in the castle were asleep.

The cows and sheep in the fields were asleep.

But as Oj ran towards the castle gates the sky lightened and the sun rose from behind the hill. The owl and the badger and the moths and the mice went to bed, and everyone else woke up and got up.

When Oj ran into the castle he was so breathless that at first he could only whisper, "A star is falling onto the castle." The people were too busy getting ready for market day to listen.

"Tell your funny stories to the sheep," grunted the King's guard, without even looking up.

"Lazy layabout," yelled the Queen's cook, "Don't waste our time with your nonsense. Get back to your work."

So Oj went back to the hillside, where he played soothing music to his sheep while he watched a whirling twirling silvery bright egg float down and land on top of one of the castle towers.

The people in the castle didn't like it. They wanted to destroy it.

They called for the soldiers, who blunted their axes and dented their swords without even denting it.

They called for the council who talked about it for days.

They called for the Queen who suggested cooking it with bonfires. It didn't even get warm.

They called for the King who suggested using levers.

He said, "All push together when I say PUSH." So they did.

Oj watched from the hillside as the great shiny silver egg toppled off the tower top, and rolled end over end, faster and faster down the hill slope.

At the bottom of the hill grew a huge old oak tree.

SMASH crackle clatter SPLAT.

And there it was. Sitting among the roots and broken pieces of silver egg shell, with its head among the leaves, was a medium-sized mauve monster puffing pink steam through its nostrils and looking rather pleased.

After a week it had grown into an oak-tree-sized mauve monster, and was practising blowing pink smoke rings. Oj thought it had a friendly face.

The people in the castle didn't like it. They wanted to destroy it. They were too far away to see its face. They just thought that it looked ugly and dangerous and fearfully ferocious and frightening. And BIG.

"Monsters eat men," announced the King morosely.

"Monsters molest maidens," moaned the Queen, clutching the princess till she squeaked.

The Council argued for days about how to manage monsters.

The soldiers used up all their arrows shooting at it from the battlements. It was so big — even the cross-eyed son of the second cook hit it every time. It didn't seem to mind very much. And it kept on growing bigger.

Finally the people called for Drogo, the dragon killer, the mightiest hero in the land. The sun shone from his polished armour. His huge silver horse pranced and pawed the drawbridge. Carefully Drogo balanced the extra long silver spear which the blacksmith had made him to deal with deadly dragons.

"Ready steady go," called the King, and fearlessly the mighty knight pounded down the hill towards the monster's feet. The monster bent over him. Pink steam hid both horse and rider. The monster seemed to sigh, and the mighty knight and his silver mount were blown all the way back to the castle, coughing.

"We must make a war machine," chorused the Council.

So the people set to work. Some made ammunition in the black-smith's forge, while others built a tower with sails like a windmill, that would hurl the ammunition at the enemy as they turned.

At the bottom of the hill was a thick wood which had grown up

from the acorns hidden and forgotten by the squirrels who lived in the huge old oak tree.

Oj the shepherd boy had taken his sheep to the field behind the wood to get them away from the arrows. There he lay among the dandelions and poppies, playing dance tunes to Slick his snail friend.

A black shadow put out the light of the sun.

Slick went inside to keep dry. Enormous wet pink drips splashed onto his shell.

Oj was not afraid. He liked all animals, and he could see that the monster was miserable, so he spoke kindly to it, and played some of the soothing music that his sheep liked to hear when the fox was near. The monster stopped crying. Oj offered it different plants to eat. It liked poppies best.

Then a bird told them that the war machine was nearly ready so Oj and Slick went into the wood to hide, and the monster made itself as small as possible and crawled in behind them. The King, who was monster watching from a tower top, saw them go, and all the people in the castle were sad because they were sure that the monster would swallow Oj whole once they got into the shadow of the trees.

Inside the wood everyone had heard about the gigantic egg. Even the night animals came out of their holes that afternoon to meet them, and birds flew in from a thousand miles away just to see the famous fledgling.

Oj sat on the monster's chest playing all his happiest tunes, while Slick set off to walk from monster head to tip of monster tail. The birds all sang, and the monster made low contented musical noises through a monstrous mouthful of poppies.

Everyone in the wood was happy. Inside the castle the people aimed their war machine at the wood. The war machine was ready.

But then the monster heard another noise. From high above

the world came a wild humming sound, the sort that most ears cannot hear. It throbbed in a way that the monster remembered from inside the egg. He stretched up towards it, towering above the trees.

"Fire the war machine," yelled the King.

The monster shook himself and unfolded a brand new pair of wings that he had never thought to use before. He flapped them.

Leaves blew off the trees, and the King's Guard's match blew out. Flapping steadily the monster rose into the sky, and disappeared behind the clouds.

The people in the castle were delighted.

"Hooray," they cheered when they saw Oj come out of the wood.

"Oj the shepherd boy has frightened the monster away."

"Oh mighty and honourable Oj. Hooray for Oj."

The King gave Oj his own coat of arms, and a horse and suit of armour to go with it.

The Queen sat up all night sewing the coat of arms onto all his clothes.

The princess kept kissing him.

The Council called for a procession led by Oj, and the soldiers marched behind him.

Oj ordained that the war machine should be changed into a play machine for the children. The grown-ups played bowls with the ammunition. From then on the people in the castle held a procession and a Fair every year, on the day that Oj had frightened the monster away. Whenever anyone asked him how he had done it Oj just smiled a mysterious smile.

Meanwhile high above the world a small band of space monsters hummed happily as they flew on the thousand-year-long journey back to their own planet, where the poppies, taller than earth oak trees, sway in the singing winds which mix with the monsters humming to fill the air with strange music.

They were glad to be going home after the long hard search for the precious monster egg which had been lost in a space storm. The mother and father monster who had dropped their egg, but found their chick hatched safely and soundly after all, grinned hugely and sang the loudest as they soared steadily upwards.

Humming happiest of all was the little mauve monster, now flying safely between them. He had found earth people fearfully ferocious and frightening, and awfully mean to baby monsters. Except for Oj.

Slick was happy, too. He was the first snail in outer space.

from

SPACE TRAP

by Monica Hughes

I t began with a game of hide-and-seek, and that would never have happened either if Valerie hadn't lost her temper.

"I'm sick and tired of babysitting Susan every day of this vacation. I haven't had a moment to myself. It just isn't fair!"

Mother ran a hand through her hair and stared at her. "But, Valerie, I'm counting on you. I've got a mass of figures for the computer and I'll never catch up with her underfoot. She won't be any trouble, will you, Susan?"

Susan shook her head and nodded and looked solemnly up at Valerie's furious face. Her thumb went into her mouth. "You see," Mother went on. "Good as gold. And what else would you do today anyway?"

Valerie glared. The infuriating thing was that Mother was right. There wasn't anything special to do on DeePee Three, except go out on soil testing expeditions with Father, and he was bound to take Frank again. Frank got to do all the exploring. It wasn't fair. Sometimes she felt that being the middle person in the family was too much to bear.

Frank bossed her and got all the fun of field trips with Father, and Susan got spoiled by everyone and she had to look after her. Valerie gave a huge sniff and bolted to the bathroom.

When she had had a good cry, she washed her face in the teacupful of water that the dispenser grudgingly trickled into the portable basin and stared at her tear-splotched face in the mirror.

"What an ugly skinny beast you are," she told her reflection. "No wonder nobody likes you." She thought grudgingly of Frank, who was tall, handsome and always, it seemed, in charge of his fate; and she thought of Susan, whose fair curly hair and enormous blue eyes made grown-ups croon over her until Valerie felt sick.

"I hate them. It just isn't fair." She leaned against the bathroom partition and imagined a world in which there was only Mother and

Father and herself, Valerie Josephine Spencer, the most beautiful girl in the whole Federated Galaxy, long blond hair, large blue eyes with lashes you could really notice, and a figure that went in and out, instead of being like a twig.

As always she came out of her dream feeling horribly guilty. "I don't really wish they weren't there," she told God or whoever was listening. "It's just that life's so horribly unfair."

Really, Valerie, the better half of her mind argued back to the snarky half, Mother and Father didn't have to bring you on this field trip. They could have left you back on Eden, spending the whole summer holidays in school. That happened to lots of University kids whose parents went on Planet Changing Expeditions.

"You're lucky to be here at all," she told her reflection firmly and went back to the main part of the Expedition's tent to apologize.

Mother beat her to it. "I *am* sorry, Val. You're quite right. I've been taking you for granted quite shamelessly. Frank should do his share."

"Oh, come on, Mum." Frank's voice was as deep as Father's. He stroked his new moustache. "I'm a bit old for babysitting, don't you think? Anyway Dad and I plan to go up-country today. I mean this is good stuff, really useful for school, isn't it, Dad?"

Father nodded, not really listening. He had his coffee cup in his left hand and his right hand checked off the list he'd spread across the table. Valerie felt herself starting to boil again. In just a minute she was going to start screaming, at Frank, at Father for not paying attention when it was important, at the whole world.

Before she could blow up, Mother intervened. "You've been out with your father every day so far, Frank, and Val hasn't had a minute to herself. This is the thirty-second century, after all. Women have some rights. Today you're going to have to look after Susan for a change and Val shall have a day off."

Valerie looked at Father, longing for him to say, "Why don't you come with me, Val? You'd be a real help."

But he just pushed back his chair, picked up his papers and said, "Well, I'm off."

She opened her mouth to ask him if she could go and then shut it again. She stood and watched him leave the tent. She listened to the whine of the floater's engine warming up. Go on, run out and ask him. He might say "yes." But she wouldn't ask because she was afraid that he'd say she'd only be in the way.

"Come on, Susan," said Frank in a put-on jolly voice. "Let's go and find some fun." He glared at Valerie, swung Susan onto his shoulders and galloped off with her screaming happily and kicking his chest with her feet.

Just Mum and me, thought Valerie. Perhaps she'll spend the day with me and we can talk and share feelings, woman to woman, sort of . . . . But Mother just swept the breakfast things away and turned to the computer console that filled one wall of the living part of the big tent. "Enjoy your day off, love," she said over her shoulder and began punching keys. Well, I might as well talk to the wall, Valerie thought bitterly and drifted outside.

What *was* she going to do by herself for a whole day? Being with Father was what she'd really wanted all along. Like Frank. But he was in High School and she was still only in Primary and didn't know the first thing about Planetary Reconstruction. I'd have just been in his way, she thought gloomily. That's why he zoomed off in a hurry without waiting for me to ask if I could go too.

She scuffed through the grey dust and sat down on a grey pudding-shaped boulder. Really, this is the dullest looking planet I've ever seen, and I was twelve on July 12, 3114 and I've been planet-hopping every summer since I was as old as Susan. That makes seven years, since she's five. The planet was so dull it didn't even have a name yet. The Federation called it Delta Parvonis Three, which just meant that it was the third planet of Delta Parvonis, a rotten little sun that barely kept the planet warm enough to be comfortable.

Valerie looked across the grey plain at the distant grey mountains, and kicked her heels against the grey rock. About two hundred metres away Frank was helping Susan climb the one hill, which really wasn't a hill at all but a pile of squarish rocks almost like a pyramid, all intergrown with wiry grey brush. Susan was screaming with laughter as Frank hauled her up from rock to rock. It would be fun to join in. But she couldn't really, not after making all that fuss about wanting to have some peace on her own.

She listened to the laughter and stared at the boring greyness of DeePee Three. Maybe it would be more interesting if she were a scientist. Perhaps she would be one when she grew up. Maybe she'd be famous, the first person to develop a large-scale matter-transmitter that really worked. They'd give her the Nobel Prize. She imagined the crowds cheering and her acceptance speech: "It was nothing really . . ."

Frank and Susan were making so much noise that she just had to turn around and see what they were up to. They were at the summit of the pyramid and Susan was on Frank's shoulder, pointing at something, she couldn't see what. Then they scrambled down to the plain and galloped off towards the old thorn thicket and vanished out of sight around the far side. After a while she couldn't hear their voices anymore. In fact it was so quiet you could have heard an insect chirp, if there'd been any insects on DeePee Three.

She strolled casually over to the hill and began to climb it herself. The blocks were almost as square as if they'd been shaped and put there by people, which was nonsense, because nothing and nobody had ever lived on DeePee Three. The wiry brush growing in the crevices scratched her wrists and ankles. By the time she was halfway up she wondered why she was bothering. But Frank had climbed it. What he could do she could too. She struggled on and scrambled triumphantly to her feet on the topmost block, covered with grey grit and with two broken fingernails.

It had better be worth it, she thought, turning around to see the view. But it wasn't. The same grey landscape she knew and hated at ground level. What a waste of time! Then she noticed the thorn thicket. How very peculiar! From up here you could see that it wasn't just any old thorn thicket, but it had been deliberately planted in a perfect circle. Which didn't make any sense at all, because who could have planted it?

It was unnaturally quiet. It wasn't like Susan to be quiet for this long, Unless they were playing hide-and-seek behind the thorn edge. That's it, she told herself, as she began to climb down. In just a minute Frank will "find" Susan and she'll scream and everything'll be ordinary again.

She slithered the last few metres to the ground. There still wasn't a sound. Perhaps they're waiting for *me* to find them, she thought, suddenly happy. Perhaps that's the game. She ran across the dusty plain to the thicket. After all, she told herself, if Susan wants me to play I can't disappoint her just because it's my day off.

She began to walk around the perimeter of the thicket. On the far side was a gap, like an entrance, but when she peeked in all she could see was more hedge. She ran all the way around the outside of the thicket and back to the entrance. No sign of Frank or Susan.

How quiet it was! The dry thorn bushes crackled briefly. Was that a stifled giggle or had she imagined it? "I see you," she called out, and her voice sounded very small in the grey indifferent silence. "I'm coming to get you," she threatened. She listened. A thorn rasped across the sleeve of her jumpsuit and she started. How loudly her

heart was beating! Silly, she told herself. It's only a game of hide-and-seek. She stepped through the opening. Ahead of her was a wall of thorn bush, but to left and right a passage curved out of sight. She turned briskly to the right. When an opening appeared in the inside wall of the thorn bush she took it, and found she was facing yet another wall, with passages curving away to left and right.

What was going on? Then a memory clicked in her mind. It was a maze, like the ones she'd read about in ancient Europe back on Earth. They went round and round with openings leading in to the secret centre. But only one way would actually get you there. Every other passage would come to a dead end, or lead you back to a passage already explored so you went round in a circle.

This was more like it! She could bet that Frank and Susan had already found the way to the secret centre and were waiting there for her right now. She looked for footprints in the grey dust. There were scuff marks everywhere as Susan had run to and fro, but there wasn't a definite track to follow.

Never mind. I'll take alternate left and right turns and see what happens, she told herself. Come on, Val, show them!

It worked beautifully at first and she had penetrated four of the hedge rings before she came to a dead-end and had to turn back. She was getting warm and was awfully thirsty. It must be nearly lunch-time. But Frank and Susan were still waiting for her at the centre. She had to go on.

She broke off a thorn, a wicked silver thing ten centimetres long, and made an X in the middle of the passage. There, I'll know not to try that way again. As she straightened up she saw, marked on the trunk of a thorn bush, a strange sign.

$$\underline{\text{III}}$$

It seemed to have burned into the wood. It was like no Galactic script Valerie had seen before. Frank couldn't have made it. So who had? Who else had discovered the secret of the maze? On this empty planet?

She felt cold and shivered suddenly. She looked up to see if a

cloud had covered the sun. But of course the cloud was always there, and it really wasn't cold at all. She was just letting her imagination run away with her, thinking that around the next bend, or the turning after that, there would be *something* waiting ready to jump out on her.

She swallowed and told herself not to be stupid. The whole surface of DeePee Three had been scanned before they had landed. The instruments said that without a shadow of a doubt there was nothing that ran or wriggled or bit. No animal nor reptile nor bird nor insect. Maybe some microbes, but nothing larger than that.

Valerie stuck her hands in her pockets and whistled as she walked along, keeping up her courage. The path swooped from left to right, sometimes going halfway round the circle before admitting her to an inner passage. She marked each dead-end with a thorn and glimpsed again the mysterious marking:

$$\underline{III}$$

She'd been in this place ages. How was Frank keeping Susan quiet all this time? It was more than she'd ever been able to do.

The quality of light changed and she realized that just beyond where she stood was the centre of the maze. She'd done it! She crept along the final passage. Then with a triumphant BOO! she leapt into the open centre of the maze. Only Frank and Susan weren't there, surprised that she'd made it. There was nothing but the grey dusty ground surrounded by the tight circle of thorn hedge with one opening in it, the one through which she had come.

The hedge was so tall she could see nothing above it but grey sky, with the noon sun shimmering through it. The shimmer hurt her eyes and she wondered if she were starting a headache.

"Frank! Susan! Oh, come on. Where are you? It's not funny. Game's ooo . . . ."

In the middle of her yell the ground seemed to fall away from under her with a suddenness that punched the breath out of her body. Then all the lights went out.

RECESS

COUNTING RHYMES

One-ery, two-ery, tickery, seven,
Hallibo, crackibo, ten and eleven,
Spin, span, muskidan,
Twiddle-um, twaddle-um, twenty-one.

One-ery, two-ery, ickery, Ann,
Phillisy, pholissy, Nicholas John,
Quever, quaver, Irish Mary,
Stickerum, stackerum, buck.

Intery, mintery, cutery, corn,
Apple seed and briar thorn;
Wire, briar, limber lock,
Five geese in a flock,
Sit and sing by a spring
O-U-T, and in again.

One-erum, two-erum,
Cockerum, shu-erum,
Shetherum, shatherum,
Wineberry, wagtail,
Tarrydiddle, den.

Inter, mitzy, titzy, tool,
Ira, dira, dominu,
Oker, poker, dominoker,
Out goes you.

Ala, mala, mink, monk,
Tink, tonk, toozey,
Oozy, voozy, aggardy,
Ah, vah, vack.

Eenie, meenie, mackeracka,
Hi, di, dominacka,
Stickeracka, roomeracka,
Om, pom, push.

Eenity, feenity, fickety, feg,
El, del, domen, egg,
Irky, birky, story, rock,
An, tan, toosh, Jock.

ALL THE PEOPLE WE MEET

S tories can take us places we never dreamed of visiting, and let us meet people who live so far away that we would never know them without the power of print. As we find out about how others live, we come to realize that many parts of their lives are like our own. Everyone needs to work and play, to have a place to live and food to eat, and to shape life with a family and friends. These common needs will help you to understand the various countries that you will be reading about and to appreciate and enjoy the interesting, different aspects of their lives.

For example, in this next excerpt you will meet boys from another country who want to have fun that may hurt someone else.

The Emir's son sat back in the saddle to rest his horse, and, as he looked around him, he noticed a man in a distant field bending over his work.

The Emir's son trotted his horse towards him, and, when he came near, saw that the man was indeed very old. His back was so bent that it would never be straight again.

"Old man," cried the Emir's son, "what are you planting?"

The old man was startled. Slowly and painfully he looked up and turned to face the speaker. When he saw that it was the Emir's son he bent his back once more and said, "May Allah preserve you, I am planting dates."

"Old man," cried the Emir's son, "What is your age?"

"May Allah preserve you, I have seen the time of planting

and the time of reaping now these eighty-five years."

"Well then, do you not know that it will be fifteen years before any of these trees bear fruit? Do you expect to live to a hundred so that you can taste their first harvest?"

"May Allah preserve you," replied the old one. "Others have planted and I have eaten. I, too, will plant so that others may eat."

The Emir's son stopped laughing and sat quiet on his horse.

He hardly noticed when Audu, Isa, and Iakabu rode up beside him. Their horses' flanks were heaving after the long ride, but the three friends were still ready for a laugh, and, seeing the young date trees, Iakabu leaned out of his saddle to uproot one of them. In a moment he had jerked upright again as he felt the sting of a whip across the back of his hand.

The Emir's son, his whip still raised, frowned at Iakabu and then turned to the old man. "May Allah preserve you, father," he said. "And may Allah in his bounty give your trees a rich harvest."

(from *The Emir's Son*, by Martin Ballard)

What do you think stopped the Emir's son from ruining the date trees? How did the old man help him make his decision? In our country, are there times when young people need help to act wisely? It may be that we can learn about ourselves from reading about people in other countries; that we can grow with the help of all the people we meet.

TALE OF A SHIPWRECKED SAILOR

by Ron Lynd

A long time ago in the land of Egypt, the Pharaoh sent his most trusted advisor on a special mission to a far-off land. The advisor was gone for many months, and when he returned to Egypt he was very worried. He had failed to complete his mission and he was frightened of what the Pharaoh might do to him. One of the advisor's attendants saw how upset he was and tried to make him forget his troubles.

"Take heart, my lord!" the attendant said. "We have finally reached home. Let us give praise and thanks to the gods as the mooring-post is staked and our ship is safely docked. Our crew has returned unharmed and our troops had no loss. We have left many strange places behind and in safety returned to our own land. You yourself, put on your finest clothing and go to the Pharaoh. Answer him when he questions you, and speak to the king with presence of mind. You must speak the truth. If a man is honest, his mouth can save him." The advisor just shook his head in despair, telling the attendant that nothing could save him.

The attendant was very angry and said to the advisor, "Do as you like! But before you go, let me tell you something that happened to me many years ago. I had been sent by the king to inspect his mines. I went to sea in a strong ship a hundred and twenty cubits long and forty cubits wide. One hundred and twenty sailors were in it, the pick of all Egypt. They were braver and stronger than lions. They knew the signs of the skies and could foretell a storm before it came.

"When we had been at sea for many days a storm broke before we could reach land. The sailors fought valiantly but a wave engulfed the ship, crushing the mast and sending the ship and all her crew to the bottom of the sea. I alone escaped. A wave carried me to an island. For three days I hid in the shelter of the trees not knowing what to do.

"Finally my hunger forced me to stretch my legs and search for food. The island was a paradise. I found figs and grapes, vegetables of every description, fish and many kinds of birds; the island had everything. I stuffed myself and filled my arms with food until I could carry no more. I returned to the shelter of the trees, put down my load, and with a fire drill made a fire so I could give a burnt offering to the gods.

"Then I heard a thundering noise. Trees splintered and the ground trembled. When the sounds stopped I uncovered my face and before me was an enormous snake. He was thirty cubits long and his body was overlaid with gold. His eyebrows were of real lapis lazuli and he was bent up in front like a cobra.

"As I lay on my belly before him he opened his mouth to me and, wonder of wonders, he spoke: 'Who brought you, who brought you, fellow? Tell me how you came to this island, or I shall reduce you to ashes.' I looked up into his fiery eyes and said, 'I tremble before your greatness and know not what to say.' Then he took me in his mouth and carried me to the place where he lived, and set me down unhurt.

"Once again I lay on my belly before him and he opened his mouth to me: 'Who brought you, who brought you, fellow, to this island of the sea?' Then I answered him with my arms bent before him. I said to him: 'I had set out to the mines on a mission for the Pharaoh of all Egypt. My crew knew the way of the sea and each man's heart was stouter and stronger than his mate's. A storm came up while we were at sea and a giant wave crushed the ship. Of those in it not one remained, except myself whom you see before you. I was brought to this land by a wave of the sea.'

"Then he said to me: 'Don't be afraid, don't be afraid, fellow; don't be pale-faced, now that you have come to me. It is the gods who have let you live and brought you to this island of mysteries. There is nothing that is not here: the island is full of all good things. You shall stay here for four months. Then a ship will come from your homeland with sailors in it whom you know. You shall go home with them and you will live many more years, and when you are very old you will die peacefully in your village.

" 'How happy is he who can tell of the dangers after the calamity has passed,' said the serpent. 'I shall tell you a story of what hap-

pened to me on this island. I was here with my brothers, and there were children with them. In all we were seventy-five serpents, children and brothers. Then a fiery star crashed on this island and they went up in flames through it. It so happened that I was not with them in the fire. I could have died for their sake when I found them as one heap of corpses. Now I am alone on this island. If you are brave and can control your heart for four months, you shall embrace your children, you shall kiss your wife, you shall see your home and be there among your brothers.'

"Stretched out on my belly, I said to him: 'I shall speak of your power to the Pharaoh, our king. I shall bring you precious oils, myrrh, spices, and the incense of the temples. I shall tell what happened to me, and praise gods for you in the city before the councillors of the whole land. I shall slaughter oxen for you as a burnt offering. I shall send you ships loaded with all the treasures of Egypt, as is done for a god who befriends people in a distant land.'

"He laughed at me and said: 'You are not rich in myrrh and all kinds of incense. But I am the lord of the great island Punt, and myrrh is my very own. The oils you spoke of sending abound on this

island. Moreover, when you have left this place, you will not see this island again; it will have become water.'

"I waited and waited, counting the days, and the ship came as he foretold after four months had passed. I climbed up a tall tree and looked across the sea, I recognized those that were aboard the ship. When I went to tell the giant serpent I found that he already knew. He said to me: 'In health, in health, fellow, to your home, that you may see your children. Speak well of me in your homeland; that is what I ask of you.'

"I put myself on my belly, my arms bent before him and told him that all in my village would know of his kindness to me. When I looked up spread before me were chests and cages, filled with myrrh, oils, spices, perfumes, great lumps of incense, giraffes' tails, elephants' tusks, long-tailed monkeys, baboons and all kinds of precious things. The serpent said: 'You will reach home in two months. You will embrace your wife and children and you will flourish.' Even as he spoke he moved quietly back into the forest until I could no longer see him.

"When we had sailed a short distance I looked back, but the

island was nowhere to be seen. We sailed on to Egypt and in two months' time we reached the palace of the Pharaoh, just as the serpent had told me. I told him of my shipwreck, and of the failure of my mission, and I presented him with the gifts the great serpent had given me. I was made an attendant and endowed with servants of my own. So you see, my friend, even out of adversity can come happiness!"

The advisor looked at the attendant and thanked him for his encouragement, but said to him: "Do not try to cheer me up, my friend. Who would give water at dawn to a goose that will be slaughtered in the morning?" With heavy shoulders the advisor entered the palace to speak with the king.

The attendant waited. After a short time the advisor came out of the palace with a smile on his face. He rushed to the attendant and said: "You were right, my friend. I spoke the truth to Pharaoh and he rewarded me for my honesty. He told me he would never punish a man who did his best for his king, even if he failed. Let us go and give thanks to the gods for the kindness of Pharaoh and the serpent lord of the island."

MUMMIES MADE IN EGYPT

by Aliki

The ancient Egyptians had one great wish. That wish was to live forever. Egyptians believed that after they died a new life began. They would live in their tombs as they lived on earth. They would also travel to another world to live with gods and goddesses of the dead.

Egyptians believed everyone had a ba, or soul, and a ka, an invisible twin of the person. They believed that when a person died, his ba and ka were released from his body and lived on in the tomb. The ba would keep contact with the living family and friends of the dead. The ka travelled back and forth from the body to the other world.

In order for a person to live forever, the ba and ka had to be able to recognize the body, or they could not return to it. That is why the body had to be preserved, or mummified. A mummy is a corpse that has been dried out so it will not decay. The earliest Egyptians were mummified naturally. The corpse was buried in the ground. The hot dry sand of Egypt dried out the body. The preserved body turned as hard as stone, into a fossil.

As time went on, burials became more elaborate. The dead were wrapped in a shroud of cloth or skin. They were buried in pits lined with wood or stone, or in caves. Bodies not buried directly in the sand became exposed to dampness, air, and bacteria. They decayed.

So people learned how to embalm, or mummify their dead. It took centuries of practice to perfect the art. Embalmers became so expert that the mummies they made remained preserved for thousands of years.

The ba returned to the mummy at night.

It was believed the dead traveled to the other world in a boat.

Mummification was a long, complicated, and expensive process. People were mummified and buried according to what they could afford. The poor had modest burials. Noblemen and others who served the king and his queen had elaborate burials. Pharaohs, the kings of Egypt, were the richest of all. It was believed, too, that a pharaoh became a god when he died. So pharaohs were mummified the best and buried in splendour.

It took seventy days for embalmers to prepare a body. For a royal or noble burial, embalmers worked in workshops near the tomb where the mummy would be buried. Embalmers first took out

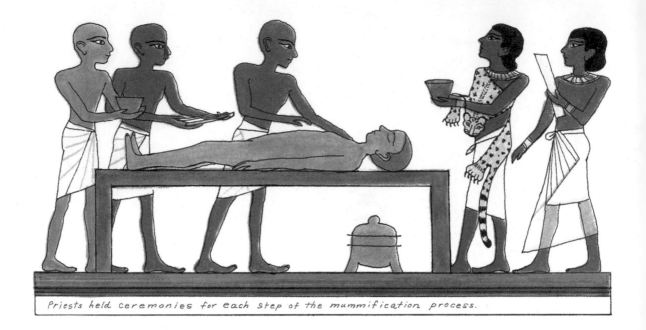

Priests held ceremonies for each step of the mummification process.

the inner organs. They removed the brain through the nostrils with metal hooks. They made a slit in the left side of the body and took out the liver, lungs, stomach, and intestines. Each of these organs was embalmed in a chemical, natron, and put in its own container called a canopic jar. The heart was left in its place.

Small bundles of natron wrapped in linen were stuffed inside the body. The outside was covered with natron, too. The chemical dried out the body the same way the sand had done. After forty days the natron packs were removed. The dried, shrunken body was sponged clean and brushed with oils, ointments, spices, and resin.

The head and body were stuffed with new packing soaked in the same substances. The eye sockets were plugged with linen and closed. The nostrils were stuffed with beeswax. The arms were crossed, and the mummy's fingernails and toenails were covered with caps of gold. The embalming cut was sewn together. The mummy was adorned with jewels of gold and precious stones.

Then the body was carefully bound with long, narrow strips of linen. Fingers, toes, arms, and legs were wrapped individually, linen shrouds were placed between the layers of binding, and every few layers were glued with resin. After twenty layers of shrouds and binding, the mummy's body took on its normal size.

It was possible, during the long process, that a piece of the corpse — an ear or a toe — would fall off. This and all leftover material

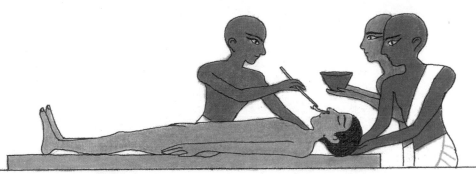

The corpse's brain was removed and probably thrown away.

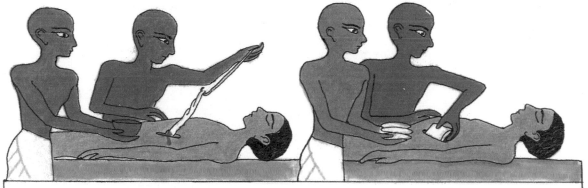

The inner organs were removed.   The body cavity was stuffed with bundles of natron.

The corpse was placed on a
slanted "embalming bed." with
a groove at the bottom.
It was covered with natron,
a grainy chemical found in
deposits in the Nile River.

Fluids from the corpse dripped
into a container as the
body dried out.

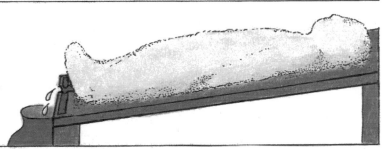

The canopic jars and the gods that guarded them:	HAPY The lungs	DUAMUTEF The stomach	IMSETY The liver	QEBHSENUEF The intestines

The internal organs were mummified separately from the body.
Each organ was wrapped in linen and covered with a mask of the god that protected it.
Then each mummified organ was put into its own canopic jar.
The lid of the jar also bore the image of the god.

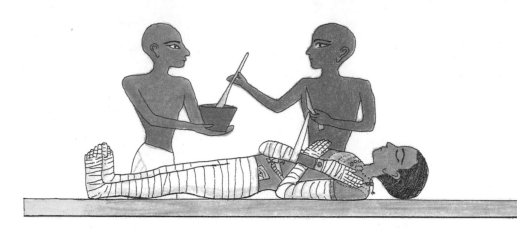

A layer of binding was covered with a shroud. Another layer of binding was placed over that, then another shroud, and so on for twenty layers. The person's name was written on the binding.

used for the embalming were saved in jars to be buried near the tomb. Magical amulets were tucked in between the mummy's wrappings. Small mummy-shaped figures called *shabtis* held farm tools. The shabtis would work in the fields of the other world for the mummy.

The bound head was covered with a portrait mask. If anything happened to the mummy, the ba and the ka would still be able to recognize it. The mask, too, was bound. Then the whole package was wrapped in a shroud and given a last coat of resin. The mummy was finished.

Meanwhile, skilled artists, sculptors, and carpenters prepared for the burial. They made the coffin or a nest of coffins for the mummy. The coffins were painted inside and out with gods, goddesses, and magic spells of protection.

They made jewellery for the mummy and furniture that would be buried in the tomb. They carved statues of the dead person to be placed in the tomb. These would serve as resting places for the ba and the ka should anything happen to the mummy. A splendid stone sarcophagus was made to hold the coffin.

A NEST OF THREE MUMMIFORM COFFINS

The mummy was put into the inner coffin. The inner coffin was covered and placed inside a second covered coffin, which fitted inside an outer coffin. The outer coffin was covered. Eventually, these coffins would be placed into a stone coffin called a sarcophagus.

Magic spells were painted on the coffins in hieroglyphs, the picture writing used by the ancient Egyptians.

The walls of the royal tombs were carved and painted with scenes that would magically come alive. The scenes show the person's new life in the other world. Dancers and musicians entertained him. Servants worked in the fields and carried food for him to eat. The gods and goddesses of the dead welcomed him.

A long, solemn funeral procession took the mummy to the tomb. The mummy rested on an elaborate sled pulled by oxen. Another sled carried the canopic jars in a chest. Priests, family, servants, and mourners, who were paid to weep, followed. Porters carried the many possessions that would be buried with the mummy.

A tomb was no longer just a pit. It was a house for the mummy, the ba, and the ka that was made to last forever. A royal tomb was also a fortress against robbers who tried to steal mummies and their treasures.

Tombs were more important than houses to Egyptians. People had them built during their lifetime. For centuries, the dead were usually buried in tombs called mastabas. Mastabas were made of brick and stone. Royal mastabas had many storage chambers and were beautifully carved and decorated.

As years went by, pharaohs took more and more with them into the tomb. Tombs became bigger, stronger, and more elaborate. For a long time pharaohs had pyramids built for themselves. Pyramids

were huge stone monuments that took hundreds of workers their lifetime to build.

The pyramid covered the pharaoh's burial chamber. Near it were temples, storage chambers, and mastabas where the royal family and servants would be buried. Later, pharaohs were buried in secret underground tombs in a deserted place that is known as the Valley of the Kings. Tunnels, passages, chambers, and the tomb itself were cut deep in rock, hidden from sight. They were magnificently carved and painted.

Then the mummy was put into the sarcophagus, which was covered with a heavy stone lid. The canopic chest, with the jars, guarded by their own gods, stood nearby. The mourners left, and the entrance of the tomb was sealed up with a wall of stone slabs.

At last, the mummy was in its eternal resting place and on the way to its new life.

QUEEN NEFERTITI

Anonymous

Spin a coin, spin a coin,
    All fall down;
Queen Nefertiti
    Stalks through the town.

Over the pavements
    Her feet go clack,
Her legs are as tall
    As a chimney stack;

Her fingers flicker
    Like snakes in the air,
The walls split open
    At her green-eyed stare;

Her voice is thin
    As the ghosts of bees;
She will crumble your bones,
    She will make your blood freeze.

Spin a coin, spin a coin
    All fall down;
Queen Nefertiti
    Stalks through the town.

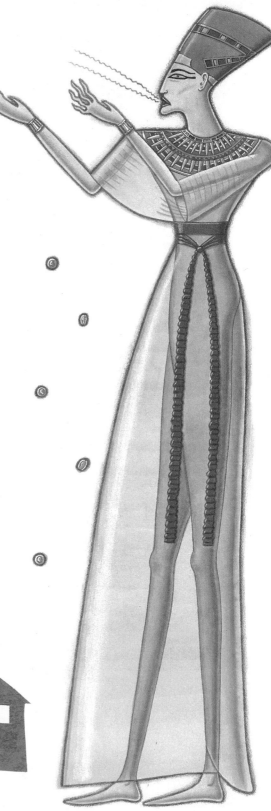

If You Should Meet a Crocodile

Anonymous

If you should meet a crocodile,
Don't take a stick and poke him;
Ignore the welcome in his smile,
Be careful not to stroke him.

For as he sleeps upon the Nile,
He thinner gets and thinner;
And whene'er you meet a crocodile
He's ready for his dinner.

The Crocodile

by Lewis Carroll

How doth the little crocodile
Improve his shining tail,
And pour the waters of the Nile
On every golden scale!

How cheerfully he seems to grind,
How neatly spreads his claws,
And welcomes little fishes in,
With gently smiling jaws!

from

A BOY CALLED NAM

by Leo Heaps

Nam, his sister Ling and their cousin Kon Ki were among the thousands of North Vietnamese people who tried to escape their unjust government in 1979. They gave their life savings to board unsafe, overcrowded boats which they hoped would take them to freedom.

Down in the filthy hold of the *Ho Chi Minh*, Kon Ki and the two children found a small space where they could barely stretch out. The damp, black interior of the boat was dense with people and already the air smelled foul. It was so dark that Nam could barely see Ling and Kon Ki although they were only inches away. It was a while before Nam's eyes grew accustomed to the dark. Never before had he been with so many strangers and crammed into so small a space. From the cries and sobbing around him, he guessed that there were many young children and infants among the men and women aboard.

Every few hours during the night a crew member descended the ladder to where the passengers lay huddled. He warned them to keep quiet and to show no lights which could be seen between the cracks in the deck planking. Otherwise the vessel might attract the attention of the officials. The government officials had been bribed, but they could always come back and ask for more money and delay the departure even longer.

Ling was frightened of the darkness and their strange surroundings.

"How long must we remain in the dark?" she asked.

"Not much longer," her brother answered. Kon Ki had fallen asleep sitting upright, as he was now unable to find sufficient room to stretch out on the wooden floorboard.

Nam tried to comfort Ling by saying, "In the morning the boat will leave; then we can all go on deck and sit in the warm sunlight and wait for the sight of the new land. There will be plenty of food there and we will all be safe."

Nam was as frightened as Ling was but he pretended that he had no fear. This helped to calm his sister, for she soon fell asleep.

Nam stayed awake peering through the gloom at the troubled faces of the people around him. He saw ordinary men and women who had put their lives into the hands of a captain who had taken all their gold and hidden them in the wet, dirty hold. Sometimes in the night Nam was startled by the cries of small children followed by the soft singing of women rocking their babies to sleep. Although he tried hard not to cry, Nam felt so lonely that tears rose to his eyes as he remembered his loving parents left behind in the village. Deep in his heart he believed he would never see his family again.

He was glad when he felt a small, friendly nudge in his back from Kon Ki, who had suddenly wakened. Kon Ki pointed to a crack in the deck planks above where the first light of day could be seen. Other families soon began to stir and waken as the engines started and the ropes holding the boat were thrown onto the deck. The refugees could feel the gentle rocking as the ship made its slow way through the harbour and into the long ocean swells.

Late in the morning a rough-looking sailor with a scraggly beard and long hair put his head down into the dark hold and ordered everyone up on deck. Nam was pleased to leave the crowded, foul-smelling dungeon, unfit for human beings to live in. He helped Ling up the ladder, followed by Kon Ki, and blinked as he entered the sunlight.

It was a warm day in September and the sea did not look as rough as it had felt when Nam lay at the bottom of the boat. Out in the fresh air and under the warm sun, the world seemed a better place. Even Ling almost smiled. They looked back to watch the dark line of mist-covered shore gradually disappear from sight.

The small boat was all by itself on the enormous sea. By the time everyone had climbed out of the hold, almost every inch of deck space was filled. More than two hundred refugees were soon lying and sitting so close together that hardly any space separated them.

In the cabin the captain stood behind the spoked wheel staring out glumly over the lumpy green water as the vessel rolled over the long, gentle swells of the South China Sea. Next to him stood his first mate and another helper who made up the entire crew of the *Ho Chi Minh*. The engine made a steady, loud chugging sound and Nam could hear the continuous clanking of the pump. Kon Ki knew that the *Ho Chi Minh* had been built only for coastal trade and was designed to carry a cargo and a small crew. It was unsuited to transporting so many people on such a difficult voyage. He prayed that the sea would remain calm but said nothing to worry his young cousins. Kon Ki told Nam that by his own calculations they should sight land near the United Nations refugee camps in about ten days' time somewhere in the area of Hong Kong. Here, he assured them, they would be welcomed and fed. In the meantime, Nam squeezed out a small space for himself and his sister near the wheelhouse, which offered a little protection from the wind.

As the sun rose higher in the cloudless blue sky, the heat steadily increased. By afternoon all the passengers, even the children, were suffering from the blistering sun, but they preferred to stay on the hot, congested deck rather than return to the darkness of the evil-smelling hold. Sometimes the spray from the waves broke over the deck, showering the refugees. The children thought this great fun and laughed, but the grown-ups were silent.

The old boat rocked from one side to the other as it dipped in and out of the troughs of the sea. Creaking and groaning from the weight of its tightly packed human cargo, it sounded like a tired old woman, her limbs stiff and cracking with every move she made.

Most of the families had children younger than Nam, who was confident he could take care of himself and his sister no matter what happened. He wandered among the other refugee children speaking to them, playing with the frightened babies, and sharing some of his food with those who had nothing to eat.

On the second day under the burning sun the little boat chugged its way across the glassy water, sailing eastward well out of sight of the South China coast. Nam knew that hundreds of other refugee boats of all sizes sailed the same waters, and that all the vessels were headed in the same direction, but he saw no other ships. He had difficulty convincing some of the passengers that they were not alone, and that somewhere just beyond the horizon others, too, were fleeing towards Hong Kong.

In the afternoon some of the children brought out small games and puzzles or found crayons and paper with which to amuse themselves, and Nam joined in the fun. After two days at sea the passengers were beginning to know one another. A kind of family atmosphere grew as people offered help or a little food or advice to their neighbours. Some of the adults had brought their mah-jong sets and dice and they began to gamble, betting money or small items like combs and earrings. No one gambled away his food.

In the hold Kon Ki found an old iron tub and triumphantly carried it on deck, where it was filled with cool sea water. The women bathed their children to temporarily cool them, but there was no place to hide from the sun which beat down mercilessly on the unprotected deck. The sea remained peaceful, except for the occasional swell which now and then rolled solidly against the boat, breaking against the hull. The passengers anxiously waited and prayed that the days would quickly pass and that the voyage would soon end.

On the tenth day of its voyage, the Ho Chi Minh *was attacked by pirates who robbed its passengers and killed two men. Throughout the next few days the boat was trapped in a violent storm and finally sank. Of the 250 refugees on board, Nam was the only survivor. He is now living in Vancouver.*

IN THE LAND
OF SMALL DRAGON

by Dang Mahn Kha

Man cannot know the whole world,
But can know his own small part.

In the Land of Small Dragon, in the Year of the Chicken, in a Village of No-Name, in the bend of the river, there were many small houses tied together by walkways. Mulberry and apricot, pear tree and flowering vines dropped their delicate blossoms on a carpet of new grass.

In a Village of No-Name lived a man and two daughters. Tâm was the elder daughter; her mother died at her birth.

A jewel box of gold and jade
Holds only jewels of great price.

Tâm's face was a golden moon, her eyes dark as a storm cloud, her feet delicate flowers stepping lightly on the wind. No envy lived in her heart, nor bitterness in her tears.

Cám was the younger daughter, child of Number Two Wife. Cám's face was long and ugly, scowling and discontented, frowning in deep displeasure. Indolent, slow and idle, her heart was filled with hatred for her beautiful sister.

An evil heart keeps records
On the face of its owner.

The father loved both daughters, one not more than the other. He did not permit his heart to call one name more dearly.

He lived his days in justice.
Standing strong against the winds.

Father had a little land, a house made of mats and clay, a grove of mulberry trees enclosed by growing bamboo, a garden and rice paddy, two great water buffalo, a well for drinking water, and twin fish ponds for the fish.

Cám's mother, Number Two Wife, cared only for her own child. Her mind had only one thought: what would give pleasure to Cám.

Her heart had only one door
And only Cám could enter.

Number Two Wife was jealous of Tâm, the elder daughter, who was beautiful and good, so the mother planned revenge on the good, beautiful child. To Cám she gave everything, but nothing but work to Tâm.

Tâm carried water buckets, hanging from her bamboo pole. Tâm carried forest faggots to burn in the kitchen fire. Tâm transplanted young rice plants from seed bed to rice paddy. Tâm flailed the rice on a rock, then she winnowed and gleaned it.

Tâm's body ached with tiredness, her heart was heavy and sad. She said, "Wise Father, listen! I am your eldest daughter; therefore why may I not be Number One Daughter, also? A Number One Daughter works, but she works with dignity. If I were your Number One the honour would ease my pain. As it is, I am a slave, without honour or dignity."

Waiting for wisdom to come, Father was slow to give answer. "Both my daughters share my heart. I cannot choose between them. One of you must earn the right to be my Number One child."

A man's worth is what he does,
Not what he says he can do.

"Go, Daughters, to the fish pond; take your fish baskets with you. Fish until night moon-mist comes. Bring your fish catch back to me. She who brings a full basket is my Number One Daughter. Your work, not my heart, decides your place in your father's house."

Tâm listened to her father and was quick to obey him. With her basket, she waded in the mud of the fish pond. With quick-moving, graceful hands she caught the quick-darting fish. Slowly the long hours went by. Slowly her fish basket filled.

Cám sat on the high, dry bank trying to think of some plan. Her basket was empty of fish, but her mind full of cunning. "I, wade in the mud?" she thought. "There must be some better way." At last she knew what to do to be Number One Daughter.

"Tâm, " she called, "elder sister, our father needs a bright flower, a flower to gladden his heart. Get it for him, dear sister."

Tâm, the good, gentle sister, set her fish basket aside and ran

into the forest to pick the night-blooming flowers. Cám crept to Tâm's fish basket, emptied it into her own. Now her fish basket was full. Tâm's held only one small fish. Quickly Cám ran to Father, calling, "See my full basket!"

Tâm ran back to the fish pond with an armload of bright flowers. "Cám," she called, "what has happened? What has happened to my fish?" Slowly Tâm went to Father bringing him the flowers and fish. Father looked at both baskets. Speaking slowly, he told them, "The test was a full basket, not flowers and one small fish. Take your fish, Elder Daughter. It is much too small to eat. Cám has earned the right to be Honourable Number One."

Tâm looked at the little fish. Her heart was filled with pity at its loneliness and fright. "Little fish, dear little fish, I will put you in the well." At night Tâm brought her rice bowl, sharing her food with the fish — talked to the thin fish, saying, "Little fish, come eat with me" — stayed at the well at nighttime with the stars for company. The fish grew big and trustful. It grew fat and not afraid. It knew Tâm's voice and answered, swimming to her outstretched hand.

Cám sat in the dark shadows, her heart full of jealousy, her mind full of wicked thoughts. Sweetly she called, "Tâm, sister. Our father is overtired. Come sing him a pretty song that will bring sweet dreams to him." Quickly Tâm ran to her father, singing him a nightbird song.

Cám was hiding near the well, watching, waiting and watching. When she heard Tâm's pretty song she crept closer to the fish, whispering, "Dear little fish, come to me! come eat with me." The fish came, and greedy Cám touched it, caught it and ate it!

Tâm returned. Her fish was gone. "Little fish, dear little fish, Come to me! Come eat with me!" Bitterly she cried for it.

> *The stars looked down in pity;*
> *The clouds shed teardrops of rain.*

Tâm's tears falling in the well made the water rise higher. And from it rose Nang Tien, a lovely cloud-dressed fairy. Her voice was a silver bell ringing clear in the moonlight.

"My child, why are you crying?"

"My dear little fish is gone! He does not come when I call."

"Ask Red Rooster to help you. His hens will find Little Fish."

Soon the hens came in a line sadly bringing the fish bones. Tâm cried, holding the fish bones.

"Your dear little fish will not forget. Place his bones in a clay pot safe beneath your sleeping mat. Those we love never leave us. Cherished bones keep love alive."

In her treasured clay pot, Tâm made a bed of flower petals for the bones of Little Fish and put him away with love.

But she did not forget him; when the moon was full again, Tâm, so lonely for her fish, dug up the buried clay pot. Tâm found, instead of his bones, a silken dress and two jewelled *hai*.* Her Nang Tien spoke again. "Your dear little fish loves you. Clothe yourself in the garment his love has given you."

Tâm put on the small jewelled *hai*. They fit like a velvet skin made of moonlight and stardust and the love of Little Fish. Tâm heard music in her heart that sent her small feet dancing, flitting like two butterflies, skimming like two flying birds, dancing by the twin fish ponds, dancing in the rice paddy.

But the mud in the rice paddy kept one jewelled *hai* for its own. Night Wind brought the *hai* to Tâm. "What is yours I bring to you." Water in the well bubbled, "I will wash your *hai* for you." Water Buffalo came by. "Dry your *hai* on my sharp horn." A blackbird flew by singing, "I know where this *hai* belongs. In a garden far away I will take the *hai* for you."

> *What is to be must happen*
> *As day follows after night.*

In the Emperor's garden, sweet with perfume of roses, the

*hai: shoes

Emperor's son, the Prince, walked alone in the moonlight. A bird, black against the moon, flew along the garden path, dropping a star in its flight.

"Look! A star!" exclaimed the Prince. Carefully he picked it up and found it was the small jewelled *hai*. "Only a beautiful maid can wear this beautiful *hai*." The Prince whispered to his heart, and his heart answered, "Find her."

> *In truth, beauty seeks goodness:*
> *What is beautiful is good.*

The Prince went to his father. "A bird dropped this at my feet. Surely it must come as truth, good and fair the maid it fits. Sire, if it is your pleasure I would take this maid for wife."

The Great Emperor was pleased with the wishes of his son. He called his servants to him, his drummers and his crier, proclaiming a festival to find one who owned the *hai*. In the Village of No-Name the Emperor's subjects heard — they heard the Royal Command. There was praise and rejoicing. They were pleased the Royal Son would wed one of their daughters.

Father's house was filled with clothes, embroidered *áo-dài** and *hai* of heavy silks and rich colours. Father went outside to sit. Cám and her mother whispered their hopes, their dreams and their plans.

Cám, Number One Daughter, asked, "Mother, will the Prince choose me?"

Mother said, "Of course he will. You will be the fairest there! When you curtsy to the Prince his heart will go out to you."

Tâm, Daughter Number Two, said, "May I go with you and Cám?" Cám's mother answered curtly, "Yes, if you have done this task: separating rice and husks from one basket into two." Tâm knew Cám's mother had mixed the cleaned rice with the unhusked.

She looked at the big basket full to brim with rice and husks. Separating the cleaned rice from that of rice unhusked would take all harvest moon time, when the Festival would end.

*áo-dài: long robes

A cloud passed over the moon. Whirring wings outsung the wind. A flock of blackbirds lighted on the pile of leaves and grain. Picking the grain from the leaves, they dropped clean rice at Tâm's feet. Tâm could almost not believe that the endless task was done.

Tâm, the elder daughter, said, "May I go? May I go, too, now that all my work is done?"

Cám taunted, "How could you go? You have nothing fit to wear."

"If I had a dress to wear could I go to the Palace?"

"If wishes were dresses, yes, but wishes are not dresses."

When Mother left she said, "Our dear Cám is ravishing. Stay at home, you Number Two! Cám will be the one to wed."

Tâm dug up the big clay pot. The dress and one *hai* were there — as soft as misty moon clouds, delicate as rose perfume. Tâm washed

her face in the well, combed her hair by the fish pond. She smoothed down the silken dress, tied one *hai* unto her belt and, though her feet were bare, hurried, scurried, ran and ran.

She ran to the Festival in the King's Royal Garden. At the Palace gates the guards bowed low before her, very low. Pretty girls stood in a line with their mothers standing near; one by one they tried to fit a foot into a small, jewelled *hai*.

Cám stood beside her mother, by the gilded throne-room door. Her face was dark and angry like a brooding monsoon wind. Cám, wiping her tears away, sobbed and whimpered and complained, "My foot fits his old shoe — everything but my big toe."

Tâm stood shyly by the door looking in great wonderment while trumpets and drummers made music for her entrance. People looked

at gentle Tâm. Everyone was whispering, "Oh! She is so beautiful! She must be a Princess fair from some distant foreign land."

Then the Prince looked up and saw a lady walking toward him. Stepping from his Royal Throne, he quickly went to meet her, and taking her hand led her to His Majesty the King.

What is to be must happen as day happens after night.

> *Real beauty mirrors goodness.*
> *What is one is the other.*

Kneeling, the Prince placed the *hai* on Tâm's dainty little foot. Tâm untied the *hai* she wore and slid her bare foot in it.

> *Beauty is not painted on.*
> *It is the spirit showing.*

The Prince spoke to his father. "I would take this maid for wife." His Royal Highness nodded. "We will have a wedding feast." All the birds in all the trees sang a song of happiness: "Tâm, the Number Two Daughter, is to be Wife Number One."

> *What is written in the stars*
> *Cannot be changed or altered.*

ETHIOPIAN PROVERBS
Traditional

To one who does not know, a small garden is a forest.

What is inflated too much will burst into fragments.

He who learns, teaches.

One who runs alone cannot be outrun by another.

Unless you call out, who will open the door?

You cannot build a house for last year's summer.

❧

When spider webs unite, they can tie up a lion.

❧

The cattle is as good as the pasture in which it grazes.

❧

When the heart overflows, it comes out through the mouth.

❧

If you offend, ask pardon; if offended, forgive.

❧

He who conceals his disease cannot expect to be cured.

NADIA THE WILLFUL

by Sue Alexander

In the land of the drifting sands where the Bedouin move their tents to follow the fertile grasses, there lived a girl whose stubbornness and flashing temper caused her to be known throughout the desert as Nadia the Willful.

Nadia's father, the sheik Tarik, whose kindness and graciousness caused his name to be praised in every tent, did not know what to do with his willful daughter.

Only Hamed, the eldest of Nadia's six brothers and Tarik's favourite son, could calm Nadia's temper when it flashed. "Oh, angry one," he would say, "shall we see how long you can stay that way?" And he would laugh and tease and pull at her dark hair until she laughed back. Then she would follow Hamed wherever he led.

One day before dawn, Hamed mounted his father's great white stallion and rode to the west to seek new grazing ground for the sheep. Nadia stood with her father at the edge of the oasis and watched him go.

Hamed did not return.

Nadia rode behind her father as he travelled across the desert from oasis to oasis, seeking Hamed.

Shepherds told them of seeing a great white stallion fleeing before the pillars of the wind that stirred the sand. And they said that the horse carried no rider.

Passing merchants, their camels laden with spices and sweets for the bazaar, told of the emptiness of the desert they had crossed.

Tribesmen, strangers, everyone whom Tarik asked, sighed and gazed into the desert, saying, "Such is the will of Allah."

At last Tarik knew in his heart that his favourite son, Hamed, had been claimed, as other Bedouin before him, by the drifting sands. And he told Nadia what he knew — that Hamed was dead.

Nadia screamed and wept and stamped the sand, crying, "Not

even Allah will take Hamed from me!" until her father could bear no more and sternly bade her to silence.

Nadia's grief knew no bounds. She walked blindly through the oasis neither seeing nor hearing those who would console her. And Tarik was silent. For days he sat inside his tent, speaking not at all and barely tasting the meals set before him.

Then, on the seventh day, Tarik came out of his tent. He called all his people to him, and when they were assembled, he spoke. "From this day forward," he said, "let no one utter Hamed's name. Punishment shall be swift for those who would remind me of what I have lost."

Hamed's mother wept at the decree. The people of the clan looked at one another uneasily. All could see the hardness that had settled on the sheik's face and the coldness in his eyes, and so they said nothing. But they obeyed.

Nadia, too, did as her father decreed, though each day held something to remind her of Hamed. As she passed her brothers at play she remembered games Hamed had taught her. As she walked by the women weaving patches for the tents, and heard them talking and laughing, she remembered tales Hamed had told her and how they had made her laugh. And as she watched the shepherds with their flock she remembered the little black lamb Hamed had loved.

Each memory brought Hamed's name to Nadia's lips, but she stilled the sound. And each time she did so, her unhappiness grew until, finally, she could no longer contain it. She wept and raged at anyone and anything that crossed her path. Soon everyone at the oasis fled at her approach. And she was more lonely than she had ever been before.

One day, as Nadia passed the place where her brothers were playing, she stopped to watch them. They were playing one of the games that Hamed had taught her. But they were playing it wrong.

Without thinking, Nadia called out to them. "That is not the way! Hamed said that first you jump this way and then you jump back!"

Her brothers stopped their game and looked around in fear. Had

Tarik heard Nadia say Hamed's name? But the sheik was nowhere to be seen.

"Teach us, Nadia, as our brother taught you," said her smallest brother.

And so she did. Then she told them of other games and how Hamed had taught her to play them. And as she spoke of Hamed she felt an easing of the hurt within her.

So she went on speaking of him.

She went to where the women sat at their loom and spoke of Hamed. She told them tales that Hamed had told her. And she told how he had made her laugh as he was telling them.

At first the women were afraid to listen to the willful girl and covered their ears, but after a time, they listened and laughed with her.

"Remember your father's promise of punishment!" Nadia's mother warned when she heard Nadia speaking of Hamed. "Cease, I implore you!"

Nadia knew that her mother had reason to be afraid, for Tarik, in his grief and bitterness, had grown quick-tempered and sharp of tongue. But she did not know how to tell her mother that speaking of Hamed eased the pain she felt, and so she said only, "I will speak of my brother! I will!" And she ran away from the sound of her mother's voice.

She went to where the shepherds tended the flock and spoke of Hamed. The shepherds ran from her in fear and hid behind the sheep. But Nadia went on speaking. She told of Hamed's love for the little black lamb and how he had taught it to leap at his whistle. Soon the shepherds left off their hiding and came to listen. Then they told their own stories of Hamed and the little black lamb.

The more Nadia spoke of Hamed, the clearer his face became in her mind. She could see his smile and the light in his eyes. She could hear his voice. And the clearer Hamed's voice and face became, the less Nadia hurt inside and the less her temper flashed. At last, she was filled with peace.

But her mother was still afraid for her willful daughter. Again

and again she sought to quiet Nadia so that Tarik's bitterness would not be turned against her. And again and again Nadia tossed her head and went on speaking of Hamed.

Soon, all who listened could see Hamed's face clearly before them.

One day, the youngest shepherd came to Nadia's tent calling, "Come, Nadia! See Hamed's black lamb, it has grown so big and strong!"

But it was not Nadia who came out of the tent.

It was Tarik.

On the sheik's face was a look more fierce than that of a desert hawk, and when he spoke, his words were as sharp as a scimitar.

"I have forbidden my son's name to be said. And I promised punishment to whoever disobeyed my command. So shall it be. Before the sun sets and the moon casts its first shadow on the sand, you will be gone from this oasis — never to return."

"No!" cried Nadia, hearing her father's words.

"I have spoken!" roared the sheik. "It shall be done!"

Trembling, the shepherd went to gather his possessions.

And the rest of the clan looked at one another uneasily and muttered among themselves.

In the hours that followed, fear of being banished to the desert made everyone turn away from Nadia as she tried to tell them of Hamed and the things he had done and said.

And the less she was listened to, the less she was able to recall Hamed's face and voice. And the less she recalled, the more her temper raged within her, destroying the peace she had found.

By evening, she could stand it no longer. She went to where her father sat, staring into the desert, and stood before him.

"You will not rob me of my brother Hamed!" she cried, stamping her foot. "I will not let you!"

Tarik looked at her, his eyes colder than the desert night.

But before he could utter a word, Nadia spoke again. "Can you recall Hamed's face? Can you still hear his voice?"

Tarik started in surprise, and his answer seemed to come

unbidden to his lips. "No, I cannot! Day after day I have sat in this spot where I last saw Hamed, trying to remember the look, the sound, the happiness that was my beloved son — but I cannot."

And he wept.

Nadia's tone became gentle. "There is a way, honoured father," she said. "Listen."

And she began to speak of Hamed. She told of walks she and Hamed had taken, and of talks they had had. She told how he had taught her games, told her tales and calmed her when she was angry. She told many things that she remembered, some happy and some sad.

And when she was done with the telling, she said gently, "Can you not recall him now, Father? Can you not see his face? Can you not hear his voice?"

Tarik nodded through his tears, and for the first time since Hamed had been gone, he smiled.

"Now you see," Nadia said, her tone more gentle than the softest of the desert breezes, "there is a way that Hamed can be with us still."

The sheik pondered what Nadia had said. After a long time, he spoke, and the sharpness was gone from his voice.

"Tell my people to come before me, Nadia," he said, "I have something to say to them."

When all were assembled, Tarik said, "From this day forward, let my daughter Nadia be known not as Willful, but as Wise. And let her name be praised in every tent, for she has given me back my beloved son."

And so it was. The shepherd returned to his flock, kindness and graciousness returned to the oasis, and Nadia's name was praised in every tent. And Hamed lived again — in the hearts of all who remembered him.

THE KING'S FOUNTAIN

by Lloyd Alexander

A king once planned to build a magnificent fountain in his palace gardens, for the splendour of his kingdom and the glory of his name. This fountain, however, would stop all water from flowing to the city below.

A poor man heard of it, and said to his wife:

"Soon our children will cry for water, our animals will sicken, and all of us will die of thirst."

His wife answered:

"A man of highest learning must go to the King, speak to him out of wisdom, and show him the folly of his plan."

So the poor man went throughout the city, to the most learned of scholars, and begged him to plead the cause. But the scholar, deep in his own grand thoughts, barely listened. He pondered lofty matters and had no interest in humbler ones. And the scholar lectured him with so many cloudy words that the poor man could make no sense of them at all, and went away downcast, saying to himself:

"Alas, the grandest thought quenches no thirst. Besides, what good is all the learning in the world if there is no one who can understand it?"

He realized that someone must present the cause clearly and winningly, with a golden tongue, so the King would listen and agree.

So he went to the marketplace, to the merchants whose words were smooth as pearls and who could string them together endlessly. But when these merchants heard what he wanted, they choked with fear and their glib words failed them. While they gladly offered clever advice, not one dared face the King.

The poor man left them and went away dismayed, saying to himself:

"Alas, the finest words are empty air without the deeds to fill them. Besides, what good is a golden tongue without a brave heart?"

Then he realized that a man of strength and courage must go

and force the King to change his plan.

Again he went throughout the city, to the strongest of all brave men: a fearless metalsmith who could knot an iron bar as easily as a shoestring.

The metalsmith, eager to stand against the King, swore that once inside the palace he would smash every window, crack every wall, and break the King's throne into firewood.

The poor man sadly shook his head, knowing the palace guards would strike down the rash metalsmith before he did even one of those deeds. And the King in his wrath would be all the more determined to build his fountain. So, leaving the metalsmith still pounding his fists, he went away in despair, saying to himself:

"Alas, the strongest hand is useless without a wise head to guide it. Besides, what use is all the bravery in the world if it serves no purpose?"

He trudged home, hopeless and heavy-hearted, and told his

neighbours and his family that he could find no one to stop the building of the fountain. His daughter spoke then, and said:

"But, Father — why not go yourself?"

Confused, unable to answer, the poor man looked at the faces of his wife and family. At last, he bowed his head and murmured:

"I hear my own flesh and blood. Indeed, there is no one else, and I myself must go to the King."

The poor man left his home. Alone, he slowly climbed the steep and seemingly endless hill. Finally, he reached the King's high palace and for a long while stood outside, fearful and hesitant.

When the palace guards roughly seized him and threatened his life for intruding, the poor man trembled in such terror he could hardly speak. Desperately he blurted out that he had an important message for the King alone.

The guards marched him to the throne room, where the King angrily demanded why he had come. Knees knocking, teeth chat-

tering, the poor man began to tell as well as he could of the suffering that the fountain would cause.

"Enough!" roared the King. "How dare you question what I do? I am the King!" The poor man wished for the smallest crumb of the scholar's learning, but he could only stammer:

"Majesty — thirst is thirst, a poor man's no less than a king's." Then his tongue dried in his mouth and he wished for even one of the merchant's golden words. The King looked scornfully at him. "You come to trouble me for that? I need only snap my fingers and my swordsmen will cut you to pieces and be done with you."

The poor man wished for one drop of the metalsmith's bravery. With his own last ounce of courage, he answered:

"You have the power to kill me. But that changes nothing. Your people will still die of thirst. Remember them each time you see your splendid fountain."

The King started up, ready to call his guards. But he stopped and fell silent for a time, his frowns deep as his thoughts. Then he replied:

"You are too simple for clever debate with me; but you have a wiser head than a scholar. Your speech is halting; but there is more true eloquence in your words than in the golden tongue of a cunning counsellor. You are too weak to crack a flea; but you have a braver heart than anyone in my kingdom. I will do as you ask."

The poor man returned to the city and told the news to all. The scholar wrote a long account of the matter in one of his books, and misplaced it. The merchants never stopped ornamenting tales of the poor man's deed. The metalsmith was so excited he tossed his anvil into the air and broke one of his own windows.

The poor man, glad simply to be home with his rejoicing family, was hardly able to believe what he had done.

"A wise head? A golden tongue? A brave heart?" he said to himself. "Well, no matter. At least none of us will go thirsty."

SONGS

JIM-A-LONG JOSIE

Barley, barley, buckwheat straw,
Hazelnuts and a cross-cut saw.
Hi Jim-a-long, Jim-a-long Josie,
Hi Jim-a-long, Jim-a-long Jo.

    I went to the river and I couldn't get across.
    I paid five cents for an old grey horse.
    Hi Jim-a-long, Jim-a-long Josie,
    Hi Jim-a-long, Jim-a-long Jo.

        Any pretty girl that wants a beau
        Fall in the arms of Jim-a-long Jo.
        Hi Jim-a-long, Jim-a-long Josie,
        Hi Jim-a-long, Jim-a-long Jo.

DO YOUR EARS HANG LOW?

Do your ears hang low?
Do they wobble to and fro?
Can you tie them in a knot?
Can you tie them in a bow?
Can you throw them over your shoulders?
Can you pluck a merry tune?
Do your ears hang low?

DOWN BY THE BAY

Down by the Bay
Where the watermelons grow,
Back to my home
I dare not go.
For if I do
My mother will say:
Did you ever see a bee
With a sunburned knee
Down by the bay?

Down by the Bay
Where the watermelons grow,
Back to my home
I dare not go.
For if I do
My mother will say:
Did you ever see a cow
With a green eyebrow
Down by the bay?

Down by the Bay
Where the watermelons grow,
Back to my home
I dare not go.
For if I do
My mother will say:
Did you ever see a witch
Digging in a ditch
Down by the bay?

Acknowledgements

Vasilisa the Beautiful: Reprinted with permission of Macmillan Publishing Company from VASILISA THE BEAUTIFUL translated from the Russian by Thomas P. Whitney. Text, Copyright © 1970 by Thomas P. Whitney. *Greyling:* By Jane Yolen, text copyright © 1968 by Jane Yolen, reprinted by permission of Philomel Books, *Dawn:* By Molly Bang. Copyright © 1983 by Molly Bang. By permission of William Morrow & Company. *Tell Me, Tell Me, Sarah Jane:* From FIGGIE HOBBIN by Charles Causley, Macmillan. Reprinted by permission of David Higham Associates Ltd. *Little John Bottlejohn:* By Laura E. Richards. By permission of Little, Brown and Company. *Ti-Jean and the White Cat:* From CANADIAN FAIRY TALES, retold by Eva Martin, Groundwood Books/Douglas & McIntyre 1984. *Halibut Man and the House on the Waves:* From THE TALKING STONE edited by Dorothy de Wit. Copyright © 1979 by Dorothy de Wit. By permission of Adriaan de Wit, for the Estate of Dorothy de Wit. *The Fish of the Sea:* From SINGING OUR HISTORY edited by Edith Fowke and Alan Mills. Copyright © 1984 by Edith Fowke. Reprinted by permission of Doubleday & Company, Inc. *The Will:* © 1973, 1976 Ian Serraillier, from I'LL TELL YOU A TALE Puffin Books. By permission of Ian Serraillier, *The Winter Wren:* By Brock Cole. Copyright © 1984 by Brock Cole. Reprinted by permission of Farrar, Straus & Giroux, Inc. *The Flying Horse Machine:* by Barbara Winther. Reprinted by permission from PLAYS FROM FOLKTALES OF AFRICA AND ASIA, by Barbara Winther. Copyright © 1976 by Barbara Winther. Publishers: Plays, Inc., Boston, MA 02116, U.S.A.

Trouble in the Jungle: Extract from TROUBLE IN THE JUNGLE by John Rowe Townsend (J.B. Lippincott Co.) Copyright © 1961 by John Rowe Townsend. By permission of Harper & Row, Publishers, Inc. *Old MacDonald Had An Apartment House:* Judith Barrett and Ronald Barrett, excerpted and illustrated from OLD MACDONALD HAD AN APARTMENT HOUSE. Text copyright © 1969 Judith Barrett. Illustrations copyright © 1969 Ron Barrett. Used by permission of Atheneum Publishers, Inc. *The Rainbow Connection:* By Paul Williams and Kenny Ascher. © 1979 Henson Associates, Inc. All Rights Reserved. Used by permission. *When I Was Young in the Mountains:* By Cynthia Rylant. Text copyright © 1982 by Cynthia Rylant. Reprinted by permission of the publisher, E.P. Dutton, a division of New American Library. *A Revolving Door:* By Lola Sneyd © Lola Sneyd. *Storm Over Lake Ontario & Street Action:* By Lola Sneyd © Lola Sneyd from the book THE CONCRETE GIRAFFE, Published by Simon & Pierre Publishing Co. Ltd./Les Éditions Simon & Pierre Ltée., PO Box 280, Adelaide St. Postal Stn., Toronto, Ontario M5C 2J4. *Home:* By permission of Douglas Young. *The General:* Exerpt from THE GENERAL by Frank Etherington. © 1983, published by Annick Press Ltd. Toronto. *The Unbelievable & Nobody's Told the Birds:* Reprinted from COLLECTED POEMS OF RAYMOND SOUSTER by permission of Oberon Press. *Peewee:* By permission of Suzanne Martel. *Gretzky:* © Meguido Zola.

Stig of the Dump: By Clive King published by Puffin Books Ltd. *Patrick's Dinosaurs:* By Carol and Donald Carrick. Text copyright © 1983 by Carol Carrick. Illustrations copyright © 1983 by Donald Carrick. Reprinted by permission of Ticknor & Fields/Clarion Books, a Houghton Mifflin Company. *Dinosaurs:* From DINOSAURS, A LOST WORLD by Keith Moseley. Reprinted with permission of Intervisual Communications, Inc., Los Angeles, CA. *Highway Construction:* By Carol Earle Chapin. © 1957 The Atlantic Monthly Co. Boston, MA. 02116. *Long Gone:* From ZOO DOINGS by Jack Prelutsky. Copyright © 1967, 1983 by Jack Prelutsky. By permission of Greenwillow Books (A Division of William Morrow & Company). *People of the Buffalo:* How the Plains Indians Lived: By Maria Campbell, Douglas & McIntyre, 1976, 1983. *Buffalo Woman:* Reprinted with permission of Bradbury Press, an affiliate of Macmillan, Inc. from BUFFALO WOMAN by Paul Goble. Copyright © 1984 by Paul Goble. *Red River Cart Song:* By permission of Lorraine Johnson. *Little House on the Prairie:* Chapter 1 "Going West" and 3 illustrations from LITTLE HOUSE ON THE PRAIRIE by Laura Ingalls Wilder, Pictures by Garth Williams. Text Copyright 1935 by Laura Ingalls Wilder; renewed 1963 by Roger L. MacBride. Pictures Copyright renewed 1981 by Garth Williams. By permission of Harper & Row, Publishers, Inc. *A Letter From the Coast:* San Francisco, September 13, 1915 (pp. 50–52) in WEST FROM HOME: Letters of Laura Ingalls Wilder, San Francisco, 1915, edited by Roger Lea MacBride. Copyright © 1974 by Roger Lea MacBride. By permission of Harper & Row, Publishers, Inc. *That Scatterbrain Booky:* By Bernice Thurman Hunter. Copyright © 1981 by Bernice Thurman Hunter. Reprinted by permission of Scholastic-TAB Publications, Richmond Hill, Ont.

Mrs. Frisby and The Rats of NIMH: Robert C. O'Brien, excerpted from MRS. FRISBY AND THE RATS OF NIMH. Copyright © 1971 Robert C. O'Brien. Reprinted with the permission of Atheneum Publishers, Inc. *Robots:* From THE KIDS' WHOLE FUTURE CATALOG, by Paula Taylor. Copyright © 1982 by Paula Taylor. Reprinted by permission of Random House, Inc. *Tomorrow:* Words by Martin Charnin. Music by Charles Strouse. © 1977 by Charles Strouse and Edwin H. Morris & Co. A Division of MPL Communications, Inc. All rights of Charles Strouse Administered by The Songwriters Guild. *The Iron Man:* Reprinted by permission of Faber and Faber Ltd. from THE IRON MAN: A Story in Five Nights by Ted Hughes. *Tell Me a Story:* From A WORD OR TWO WITH YOU by Eve Marriam. Copyright © 1981 by Eve Merriam. All rights reserved. *Future Story:* © Fiona French 1983. Reprinted from FUTURE STORY by Fiona French (1983) by permission of Oxford University Press. *Zachary Zed:* © James Reeves Estate. Reprinted by permission of The James Reeves Estate. *U.F.O.:* From U.F.O. by Joanna Stubbs. Reprinted by permission of André Deutsch Ltd. *Space Trap:* By Monica Hughes, Groundwood Books/Douglas & McIntyre 1983.

The Emir's Son: Excerpt from THE EMIR'S SON by Martin Ballard. Reprinted by permission of Longman Young Books Ltd. *Tale of a Shipwrecked Sailor:* By permission of Ron Lynd. *Mummies Made in Egypt:* Entire text and selected art MUMMIES MADE IN EGYPT, Written and Illustrated by ALIKI (Thomas Y. Crowell Co.) Copyright © 1979 by Aliki Brandenberg. By permission of Harper & Row, Publishers, Inc. *Queen Nefertiti:* From THE RANDOM HOUSE BOOK OF POETRY FOR CHILDREN, selected and edited by Jack Prelutsky. Courtesy of Random House, Inc. *A Boy Called Nam:* From A BOY CALLED NAM © 1984 Leo Heaps. Reprinted by permission of Macmillan of Canada, a Division of Canada Publishing Corporation. *In the Land of Small Dragon:* Told by Dan Manh Kha to Ann Nolan Clark. Copyright © 1979 by Ann Nolan Clark. Reprinted by permission of Viking Penguin Inc. *Ethiopian Proverbs:* Reprinted by permission from AFRICAN PROVERBS, copyright 1962, 1985, Peter Pauper Press, Inc. *Nadia the Willful:* From NADIA THE WILLFUL, by Sue Alexander, pictures by Lloyd Bloom. Copyright © 1983 by Sue Alexander. Illustrations Copyright © 1983 by Lloyd Bloom. Reprinted by permission of Pantheon Books, a division of Random House, Inc. *The King's Fountain:* By Lloyd Alexander, illustrated by Ezra Jack Keats. First published, 1971, in the U.S. by E.P. Dutton. All rights reserved under International and Pan-American Copyright Conventions. Reprinted by permission of the publisher, E.P. Dutton, a division of New American Library.

Care has been taken to trace the ownership of copyright material used in this text. The publishers welcome any information enabling them to correct any reference or credit in subsequent editions.